A FIELD GUIDE TO

Desert Holes

Lenore Rutti

A FIELD GUIDE TO

Desert Holes

BY PINAU MERLIN

ILLUSTRATIONS BY

PAMELA ENSIGN

CONTRIBUTORS

Peter Siminski
ASDM Director of Living Collections

Craig Ivanyi
ASDM Collections Manager of Herpetology

Barbara Terkanian
ASDM Collections Manager of Invertebrates

ARIZONA-SONORA DESERT MUSEUM PRESS

TUCSON • ARIZONA

Published in the United States by Arizona-Sonora Desert Museum
2021 N. Kinney Road, Tucson, Arizona 85743
http://www.desertmuseum.org

This book is available at quantity discounts for educational,
business, or sales promotional use. For further information,
please contact:
ARIZONA-SONORA DESERT MUSEUM PRESS
2021 N. Kinney Road, Tucson, AZ 85743
(520) 883-3028

SERIES AND BOOK EDITOR: Steven Phillips
BOOK AND COVER DESIGN: Steven Phillips
COVER PHOTO: John Hoffman
ILLUSTRATIONS: Pamela Ensign
PRINTED IN CANADA BY HIGNELL PRINTING LIMITED

1 2 3 4 5 6 7 8 9

ISBN 1-886679-12-6

CONTENTS

ACKNOWLEDGMENTS

Many thanks go to Peter Siminski, ASDM Director of Living Collections, not only for lending his expertise to this project but also for coming up with the book's concept. A number of years ago Peter produced a small guide on desert holes, which was published in the spring 1994 issue of the Desert Museum's membership magazine *sonorensis*. It was so well received that the Desert Museum decided to produce this much expanded version.

Special thanks to two other Desert Museum staff members: Craig Ivanyi, Herpetology Collections Manager, for his input on the lizard and amphibian sections of this book and Barbara Terkanian, Invertebrate Zoology Collections Manager, for her assistance with the invertebrate accounts and the illustrations.

Many other people helped in the production of this book, giving generously of their time and knowledge. I am especially grateful to Desert Museum staff members Renée Lizotte and Tom Van Devender, and to Carl Olson, Betsy Wirt, Robert Smith, and Yar Petryzian of the University of Arizona; David Pearson at Arizona State University; Steve Prchal at Sonoran Arthropod Studies Institute; Steve Buchmann, Justin Schmidt, and Heywood Spangler from the Carl Hayden Bee Lab; and Nikolle Brown.

I also want to thank copy editors Linda Gregonis and Chris Carbonaro, Pam Ensign, who worked so hard on the illustrations, and Steve Phillips, ASDM Publications Manager, for his patience and support.

P.M.

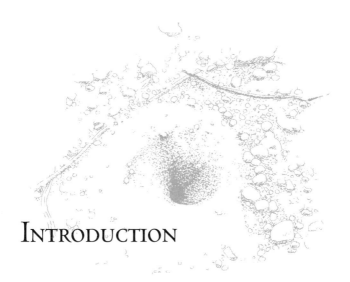

INTRODUCTION

Have you ever discovered a fresh hole in your front yard
and wondered who's taken up residence? Or walked in the
desert and noticed all kinds of holes in the ground and in
the trees and cacti and puzzled over them? If so, this book
is for you.

The tremendous diversity of wildlife species and the
fact that the ground is not usually covered over by vegetation make holes more abundant and more evident in the
desert Southwest than almost anywhere else. Some holes
are apparent because of their size, like coyote dens or
badger diggings. Others, like round-tailed ground squirrel
holes, are hard to miss simply because there are so many
of them. These holes are clues to the hidden life of the
desert, indications of an animal's presence and activity in
an area. Holes, along with tracks, scats, food remains, and
other bits of evidence can help us discover more about the
lifestyles and habits of the desert's wild inhabitants.

What may come as a surprise to many readers is that determining who is currently using a burrow is often a tricky business. That's because a great deal of borrowing and sharing goes on. A number of animals, like most snakes and burrowing owls, don't dig their own retreats, preferring to appropriate burrows left by others. Sometimes other animals may move right in with the original owner of the hole, obtaining living space but neither harming nor benefitting the owner. This is called commensalism. Other associations, where both parties benefit each other, are called mutualisms.

So although the study of holes and burrows is not an exact science, this book should help you sort through the often bewildering abundance of holes, depressions, and shelters and figure out who may have built them and possibly who's using them now.

What's Covered and What's Not

The common animals that burrow or den that you're likely to encounter in desert habitats are included in the book. Some reptile and amphibian species aren't included, because most of them don't leave an actual hole or depression. The western shovel-nosed snake, for example, swims in loose sand, but the sand collapses in as the snake moves through it, leaving no hole or burrow. The horned lizard is another reptile that burrows into loose soil at night but usually leaves little evidence of its nocturnal activities.

This field guide focuses on the Arizona and California portions of the Sonoran Desert, although it can also be used by folks in other areas of the desert Southwest. Whether you live in Albuquerque, Phoenix, or Las Vegas, in a townhouse or in a home out in the desert, you will still find much of this information useful and fun.

How To Use This Book

This field guide is designed for quick and easy identification. All you have to do is follow these simple steps.

1. Determine the location (ground or elevated), shape and size of the hole. Use the measuring guide on the last page of this book to measure holes, or carry along a small tape measure.
2. Find the appropriate section in the book. The book is divided into five sections: GROUND HOLES, DEPRESSIONS, MOUNDS, ELEVATED HOLES, and BORROWED / MODIFIED SHELTERS. Each section is arranged by size of hole from smallest to largest.
3. Check the KEY FEATURES listed for each entry to see if your hole fits that brief description.

Once you think you've found the correct entry, read the Natural History text. Many holes, like those of mice or ground squirrels, will be of a similar size and the differences can be subtle. The natural history of the animal should provide additional clues to help whittle down the choices. Tracks, which can also help determine what animal is currently using a burrow, are included for most of the bird and mammal entries.

The description of the hole or depression gives the most common dimensions, but keep in mind that these features are made by living creatures, so size will vary in different circumstances and in different locations.

We hope this book will give you enough clues and information to deduce the occupants of many desert holes. With any luck it will also give you a new and fascinating way to enjoy the magic of the desert.

GROUND HOLES

KEY FEATURES
- ► vertical shaft in ground
- ► from 6 to 18 inches deep
- ► found in moist soil in open spots

POSSIBLE BUILDER
tiger beetle (*Cicindela* spp.)

DESCRIPTION OF HOLE
Tiger beetle larvae dig vertical shafts in the ground where they lie in wait for unsuspecting insects to wander past. The larva enlarges the perfectly circular hole as it grows, to fit its head exactly. The hole is well camouflaged, as the larva uses its flat head to seal the hole while it watches for prey. Grains of sand on the top of the head complete the illusion. The hole suddenly becomes visible as you walk near it, because the larva responds to the vibrations and shadow of a large predator (you) by crawling down to the bottom of the hole.

NATURAL HISTORY
Tiger beetle adults are beautifully colored, predatory insects that catch and eat any other insects they can sub-due. They are very fast fliers. There are many species of tiger beetles found in a variety of habitats, but here in the desert Southwest they favor riparian habitats, moist areas near streams and pools, places near large boulders that hold moisture in the ground, and any habitat similar to beaches. The Willcox Playa in southeastern Arizona boasts the largest diversity of tiger beetle species (18) of any place in the United States.

The larva is an ambush predator with huge mandibles, lurking in its hole in the ground waiting to attack passing insects. The tiger beetle larva has the quickest movement of any larva known. It does a partial back flip, coming a third of the way out of its hole to grab prey of suitable size—flies, ants, even adult tiger beetles! The tiger beetle larva has a pair of hooks on its lower body that it uses to attach itself to the wall of the tunnel, and thus prevents itself from being pulled out of the hole by too large a prey item. The larva drags the prey into the hole, chews the insect with powerful mandibles, then sucks the juices out of it. The tiger beetle larva

Tiger beetle larvae

then takes the remaining ball of hard exoskeleton parts to the surface and flips it away from its burrow.

Tiger beetle larvae are preyed on by two parasites—hover flies and a methoca wasp who specializes on tiger beetle larvae. While poised above a tiger beetle hole, a hover fly flips its eggs, which roll down into the hole and attach to the back of the larva. After hatching, the new fly larva devours its host. The methoca wasp uses a different strategy, allowing herself to be caught by the tiger beetle larva, which can't crush the wasp's tough exoskeleton. She stings the larva, paralyzing it, then lays her eggs on it. The developing larvae of the wasp consume the paralyzed tiger beetle larva.

BORROWERS
none known

KEY FEATURES
► cleared area with hole in center
► may have raised cone around hole
► may have more than one hole
► may be trails leading to and from hole

POSSIBLE BUILDERS
seed harvester ant (*Pogonomyrmex* spp.)
leafcutter ant (*Acromyrmex* spp.)
army ant (*Neivamyrmex* spp.)
honeypot ant (*Myrmecocystus* spp.)

DESCRIPTION OF HOLE
Ant holes vary considerably according to the species and
size, but usually there is an area cleared of vegetation
around the hole. As some species of ants excavate their
tunnels, they dump piles of dirt outside their entrance
holes, which look like inverted cones or tiny volcanoes.
Other entrances are flat with irregularly shaped holes.

NATURAL HISTORY
There are more than 250 species of ants in Arizona alone.
A few of the common species are described here. Ants, like
bees, are social creatures who live in large colonies, all
working together for the benefit of the group. Colonies
may last for 10 to 20 years, though the individual worker
ant may only live from two months to one year. Ant
colonies consist of a queen who does all the egg laying,
and workers, who are all nonbreeding females. Males live
only briefly, during mating season. In some species the
workers are all the same size and look alike, their duties
determined by their age (only the oldest are sent out to

17

forage). In other species the workers vary in size, with shapes suited to different tasks; they are divided into castes, becoming soldiers, nurses who take care of the larvae, food gatherers, and so on.

Pheromones (chemicals that stimulate particular responses) play an important role in ant communication. Ants commonly lick each other—especially around the mouth—passing drops of liquid or food as well as chemical

Leafcutter ant hole

messages. These chemical messages tell the ants what kinds of tasks need to be done. Scouts or workers outside the nest use chemical communication as well by laying down chemical trails for the other ants to follow to find food resources.

Ants are the main food of blind snakes, who follow the ants' chemical trails to find the nest and consume its residents. Horned lizards are another major predator of ants.

HARVESTER ANT NESTS

Harvester ants don't like rocky soil, preferring creosote flats and bottomland, but they may also be found in urban areas. These large, aggressive ants usually make a clearing about 3 feet in diameter around the entrance hole to the nest, which is flat. The area is kept clear by the ants, who bite off the stems and leaves of plants that try to grow there. The hole, about 2 inches in size, is usually not perfectly round. Trails leading from the entrance may be evident.

HARVESTER ANT NATURAL HISTORY

These ½ inch black or red ants primarily collect seeds to eat and to store, but do eat other insects as well. They make caches of seeds in their underground chambers to tide them over during lean times. Sometimes harvesters plant "gardens" by removing sprouted seeds from the cache. They carry them up to the surface and dump them, where they take hold and grow. Harvester ants have a painful sting and a particularly potent venom.

LEAFCUTTER ANT NESTS

Leafcutter ants often have multiple entrances to the nest, from five or six up to eight or more. Each one has a well defined cone that is about 6 inches in diameter and 1½ to 2 inches high, though there may be an occasional entrance without a cone. Inside the nest are tunnels about the diameter of a pencil or less, with various rooms that are up to 3 feet long and 12 inches high and wide. Tunnels may be 15 to 20 feet deep!

LEAFCUTTER ANT NATURAL HISTORY

These reddish-brown ants are often seen gathering plant material and carrying it back to their nests along ant trails. They prefer ocotillo flowers and leaves, palo verde and ironwood flowers and leaves, some creosote, and leaf litter. They don't eat the plant material, but chew it up back at the nest to make a compost, which is used to grow a fungus garden. The particular species of fungus is the ants' sole food. It is carefully tended by the ants, whose saliva inhibits the growth of any other fungi. The fungus lives for the life of the colony, and when a queen ant starts a new colony, a piece of the fungus is carried by her to the new nest.

ARMY ANT NESTS
Army ants don't build their own nests with tunnels and chambers, preferring to take over an abandoned tarantula or wolf spider hole or mouse burrow. Even a hole under a rock will suffice.

ARMY ANT NATURAL HISTORY
These large black ants, about ³/₈ to ½ inch in length, are predators who actively hunt other insects and raid the nests of other ants. These nomadic ants stop for periods of about six weeks for brood production. During this resting phase, the larvae of the colony spin their cocoons, pupate, and then emerge as adult ants. At the same time, the queen lays a new batch of eggs, which hatch into new larvae. These new larvae secrete pheromones that stimulate the colony to increase food gathering to feed them, thus setting the colony on the move again. The ants march in columns, carrying the larvae with them. Side branches spread out from the center column to capture and subdue anything they find in their way.

HONEYPOT ANT NESTS
Honeypot ant nests are hard to define, with no distinctive shape and no cone. The entrance hole is about 2 inches in diameter, and could be mistaken for a harvester ant hole.

HONEYPOT ANT NATURAL HISTORY
Honeypots, about ³/₈ of an inch in length, live on sweet juices and fluids collected from plants, scale insects,

caterpillars, aphids, and other insects that secrete honey-dew. They live in the arid Sonoran Desert where these fluids are not available all year long, and so store supplies to see them through times of drought or famine. They store these reserves in the gasters, or bellies, of a caste of honeypot ants called repletes. The repletes receive the

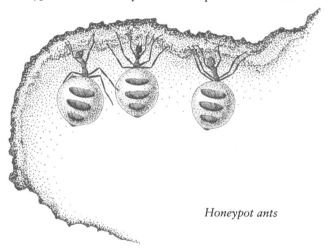

Honeypot ants

honeydew from ants returning from foraging, continuing to store more and more fluids until their abdomens swell up like grapes. The repletes are so heavy and distended that they can't move about, so they hang by claws onto the ceiling of the nest chambers and dispense honeydew to the other ants when they need it.

Native peoples dug up honeypot ant nests to eat the sweet repletes.

BORROWERS, COMMENSAL USERS
Other ants, beetles, roaches, and crickets may live in an ant nest, even while it is occupied.

21

KEY FEATURES
▸ tiny hole about ⅛ to ¼ inch
▸ small pile of soil particles around hole
▸ may be many scattered or clumped holes in an area

POSSIBLE BUILDERS
digger bee (*Diadasia* spp.)
bumblebee (*Bombus sonorus*)

NATURAL HISTORY
The Sonoran Desert is home to over 1,000 species of solitary and social bees—more than almost anyplace else in the world. Unlike European honey bees, solitary bees don't make hives with thousands of workers. Instead, each female makes her own nest and provisions it with nectar and pollen for her own eggs, although huge aggregations of the bees will use the same area.

DIGGER BEE NESTS
Digger bee holes are usually tiny, up to about ¼ inch in diameter, and show evidence of fresh digging. Some species of digger bees make a hole that has a little pile of soil granules to one side; some have concentric rings of soil around the hole; and still others create little craters with mud chimneys. The mud chimneys are thought to foil the attempts of parasitic hover flies, who flip eggs into the bee holes, where the eggs attach to the bee larvae inside. Once hatched, the fly larvae devour the bee larvae. Some of the bee holes are 6 to 12 inches deep, others can be as much as 6 to 8 feet.

DIGGER BEE NATURAL HISTORY

There are so many species of digger bees, all with different habits, that only a couple of the more common species are mentioned here. Digger bees are active for several weeks to a few months during spring and the early summer months. Some species become active when their specific plants are blooming. The cactus bee for instance, emerges during the peak of cactus flower blooming in April, May, and June to pollinate prickly pear, cholla, and saguaro.

Digger bee and nest

In some species, like the palo verde digger bee (*Centris pallida*), the male emerges first and buzzes around close to the ground, using his antennae to smell females still buried in their natal cells. The male begins digging to help the female emerge, and then mates with her as she does.

The female digger bee excavates a hole in the ground that may be a single tunnel with one or two cells or a more elaborate affair with branching side tunnels and up to 16 cells. She either polishes the tunnel walls, lines them with mud, or uses waxes secreted from her own body to seal the walls from moisture that could rot the eggs or spoil the provisions. The bee then gathers nectar and pollen to make "bee bread," which she stuffs into each individual cell. Finally, she lays an egg on the bee bread and seals the cell. After the egg hatches, the larva feeds on the bee bread and grows, then spins a cocoon, pupates, and overwinters in its cell, emerging the next spring.

BUMBLEBEE NESTS
Bumblebees don't make their own nests, instead using abandoned mouse or ground squirrel holes. In peopled areas they'll also use anything with upholstery or insulation, even old discarded mattresses.

BUMBLEBEE NATURAL HISTORY
Although their colonies are small, bumblebees are a more social bee, an intermediate step between solitary bees and the truly social honey bees. A queen bumblebee emerges in the spring, selects a mouse nest or other hole in the ground, then rearranges the grasses, fur, or fluff inside the nest. She begins secreting wax and building wax cells in clusters to use as storage pots for nectar and pollen with which to feed her larvae. The roundish wax cells are somewhat messy, lacking the neat geometrical formation of honey bee cells. The queen lays an egg or two in each cell and tends them and feeds them as they develop into larvae. When they become adult workers they take over many of the daily chores of the hive, making wax cells and storing honey. This frees the queen to lay more eggs and expand the hive, although she continues to help with these chores. At the end of summer there may be several hundred individuals. Then the new virgin queens and males leave the nest to mate, while the rest of the colony dies with the onset of winter. The males also die, but each new queen overwinters in a protected spot that she digs in a bank or finds in a wall or insulated place, emerging in the spring and beginning a new colony.

BORROWERS
none known

KEY FEATURES
► hole about 1 to 1½ inches
► slanting burrow about 12 inches long

POSSIBLE BUILDERS
pepsis wasp (*Pepsis chrysothemis*)
cicada killer wasp (*Sphecius grandis*)

PEPSIS WASP HOLES
Female pepsis wasps (tarantula hawks) dig a slanting burrow with their mandibles and front legs. The tunnel is about 12 inches long, with a chamber at the end. The hole is not often noticed because it is only open while the wasp is searching for and burying her prey.

PEPSIS WASP NATURAL HISTORY
Wasps as a family specialize in preying on other insects. They are well equipped for their predatory habits with potent venoms that paralyze their victims.

The pepsis wasp, the largest wasp in the United States, is also commonly known as the tarantula hawk, for its larvae feed entirely on tarantulas. The adult pepsis wasp feeds on nectar and pollen, and is especially attracted to milkweed flowers. The larvae are carnivorous and must be supplied with live prey on which to feed and grow.

The female pepsis wasp, a beautiful blue-black wasp with orange wings, sets about hunting for female tarantulas. She particularly wants a female as they are much larger and heavier than male tarantulas, providing more food for her offspring. The pepsis wasp searches for tarantula burrows and may go right into the hole after the spider. She lures it outside, where she tries to sting the tarantula on the underside of its abdomen in a nerve center, which paralyzes the spider. The wasp then drags its helpless victim (many times larger than herself) to her prepared hole. Occasionally she uses the tarantula's own burrow. She stuffs the tarantula in the hole and brushes the hairs off the spider's abdomen to make a clear spot.

The wasp then lays an egg on the spider's abdomen and seals up the hole in the ground. After hatching, the wasp larva feeds on the paralyzed but still living tarantula. Once the larva has grown enough, it pupates. The process from

Pepsis wasp

egg laying to pupation may take anywhere from two weeks to a few months. The pepsis wasp gathers a fresh tarantula for each egg she lays; she may lay 6 to 20 eggs in a season. Even if the wasp is disturbed and abandons the tarantula before laying an egg on it, the tarantula doesn't recover from the paralysis.

Pepsis wasps have a very potent venom and their stings are considered excruciatingly painful to people, but they are placid animals and very rarely sting.

CICADA KILLER HOLES

Cicada killers make extensive tunnels up to 12 inches long in soft, sandy soil, avoiding the hard caliche soils. Some may have up to 18 different cells or chambers along the sides of the tunnel, with a different cell for each egg. The cicada killer hole has a heap of dirt around the entrance, dug out from the tunnel. The hole is only open while the wasp is collecting cicadas and laying eggs in the tunnel.

CICADA KILLER NATURAL HISTORY

Cicada killers are large, heavy-bodied wasps that specialize in cicadas. Like the pepsis wasp, the cicada killer searches out prey to provision the nest for her larvae. Cicada killers also prefer female cicadas, because they are larger than the males. The cicada killer stings the cicada, paralyzing it, then drags the cicada to a high point on a bush or tree and flies off with it. She places the cicada in one of the cells in her tunnel and lays an egg on it. Since the female cicada killer wasp is so much larger than the male, female larvae are supplied with several cicadas and male larvae only get one or two. (Wasps, bees, and ants can control the sex of the eggs they lay. After mating, queen bees, ants, and wasps have a store of sperm that lasts them the rest of their lives. They can allow an egg to be fertilized by this stored sperm or not. If the egg is fertilized it becomes a female, if it isn't it becomes a male.) The hole is sealed up, the larvae feed on their paralyzed hosts, pupate, and emerge the next summer, coinciding with the cicada emergence in late May and June.

BORROWERS
none known

KEY FEATURES
► circular hole, 1 to 1½ inches in diameter
► nearly vertical shaft lined with silk; silk may be visible near entrance
► may be a film of silk across entrance during the day
► spider may sit at hole entrance at night

POSSIBLE BUILDER
tarantula (*Aphonopelma chalcodes*)

DESCRIPTION OF HOLE
A tarantula digs a burrow or hole in the ground about 12 inches deep with a chamber angling off at the bottom. It usually lines its hole with silk. Although no web is obvious outside the hole, strands of silk can sometimes be seen. A film of silk often covers the entrance to the hole during the day when the spider is not actively hunting for prey. The silk carries vibrations down to the spider, bringing information about what's happening above. It may also function to hold humidity in the burrow.

NATURAL HISTORY
Tarantulas are among the most recognizable animals in the desert Southwest. Their large size, about 3 inches, and hairy legs and abdomen give them an intimidating appearance, but they are calm creatures that are not aggressive toward humans. They are the largest spider in the United States, some weighing in at 1 ounce. There are several species of tarantulas in the Sonoran Desert, with different species found in desert, grasslands, and oak woodland environments. They are not web builders, but live in and

hunt from burrows in the ground.

The tarantula is a nocturnal hunter, waiting at the entrance to its hole for passing insects, particularly beetles and grasshoppers. A tarantula has poor vision, depending instead on feeling the vibrations made by its prey. The spider grabs its prey and drags it into its burrow to eat. Sometimes you can actually hear little crunching noises coming from the burrow as the spider crushes the exoskeleton of its prey before sucking out the juices.

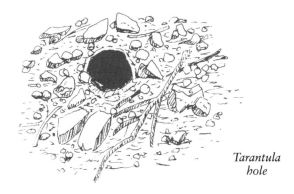

Tarantula hole

Tarantulas defend themselves from prying foxes, coyotes, raccoons, and other predators by use of urticating (irritating) hairs on the abdomen. They rub their legs against the abdomen to loosen the barbed hairs, which then find their way into the eyes or nasal passages of the predator. These specialized hairs may irritate for a couple of days, teaching most predators to treat tarantulas with respect. Coatis have learned a trick in dealing with a tarantula, however, grabbing the spider and rolling it vigorously on the ground to dislodge the urticating hairs before eating it.

Females are larger than males, are lighter colored, and

live about 20 to 25 years. The males live about 10 to 13 years, and in the last year of life wander about on rainy season nights looking for females to mate with. The males eat only opportunistically during this time and at the end of the season they die. Females can mate each year after they reach maturity, though the males only mate during their last season of life.

Mating is a precarious affair among the spiders, as the female is apt to eat the male. The male must use caution in approaching the female, announcing his intentions by strumming on the silk of her burrow or tapping on the ground with his pedipalps (modified front legs). If she is agreeable, they mate, with the male holding the female's fangs so that she cannot bite. Later, the female tarantula lays her eggs inside the burrow and wraps them in silk. After the spiderlings hatch, they remain in the burrow awhile before dispersing, but the mother doesn't provide any care or feeding.

Tarantulas are most commonly seen during humid, rainy summer nights.

BORROWERS
Army ants may take up temporary residence in an abandoned tarantula hole.

KEY FEATURES
► circular, about ¾ to 1 inch
► turret or collar of silk and twigs around entrance

POSSIBLE BUILDER
wolf spider (*Hogna carolinensis*)

DESCRIPTION OF HOLE
Wolf spider holes are a little smaller than tarantula holes, up to an inch in diameter, and instead of a film of silk across the hole entrance, the wolf spider builds a turret or collar around the hole, using silk and bits of twigs and debris. The turret may extend from ¼ inch to 1 inch above the hole. The hole can extend 12 inches or more into the ground in a spiral shape. The function of the turret is not known for certain, but flood control is a possibility.

NATURAL HISTORY
Wolf spiders are good-sized arachnids averaging 1 inch in body size with long legs. They live in a variety of habitats, from grasslands to forests, to deserts. They are nocturnal hunters, with large eyes that they use primarily to detect motion. Rather than using a web, these spiders actively hunt for small insects near their burrow and within a territory of several square feet. The male may wander further from his burrow than a female, who typically stays closer to home.

31

The wolf spider injects its prey with digestive enzymes, then chews it up with the serrated chelicerae (spider jaws) before sucking out the prey's juices. It sometimes leaves a pellet of exoskeleton parts when it is done.

Like tarantulas, male wolf spiders may wander around during rainy season nights, looking for females to mate with. The male uses a variety of signals to alert the female spider that he is a male, not a meal. He waves his pedipalps (modified front set of legs) up and down, and uses a pick and comb arrangement on the pedipalps to make sounds. He rubs the "pick" across the "comb" to produce vibrations (an activity called stridulation). Once mating has occurred, the female spins a silken bag to lay her eggs in and then attaches it to her spinnerets (two projections at the bag of her abdomen from which she spins silk) and carries it around with her. In about a month the babies hatch and climb up on the mother's back, riding there until they molt for the first time, about a month later, when they disperse.

You can often recognize wolf spiders on the road during summer nights by their green eyes reflecting from your car headlights. During the summer rainy season, when mother wolf spiders carry their young on their backs, the myriad of tiny eyes all reflecting green is a beautiful sight.

Wolf spiders may live about two years, spending the winter in a hibernation-like state called diapause. In the desert, they are active from March through October.

BORROWERS
An army ant colony may take over an abandoned wolf spider hole.

KEY FEATURES
➤ at base of tree
➤ hole almost an inch in diameter

POSSIBLE BUILDER
palo verde root borer (*Derobrachus geminatus*)

DESCRIPTION OF HOLE
Palo verde root borers leave a quarter-sized hole in the
ground as the adult beetle emerges from its underground
larval home during the summer months. The hole, with no
mound of dirt around it, is usually found under a tree.

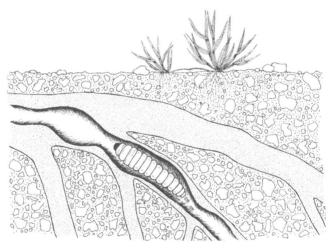

NATURAL HISTORY
At an impressive 3 to 3½ inches long, adult palo verde
root borers are among the largest beetles in the United
States. They are commonly seen flying about on rainy season nights, but are poor fliers and often crash into things.

33

They can defend themselves with a powerful bite. The adults only live for about a month or six weeks.

The larvae, though not usually seen, are even more impressive. The 5 inch long white grubs live underground, feeding on starches within the roots of various trees. Female palo verde beetles lay their eggs in the dirt at the base of a tree. Upon hatching, the larvae burrow into the ground and into tree roots, where they feed for several years. The larvae can completely hollow out a large root, leaving it filled with droppings, then move to another root by tunneling through the ground.

Palo verde root borers infest a variety of native and non-native trees, particularly those that are already stressed from the heat and aridity in the desert. Most trees can tolerate a few root borers, as the larvae don't always cut through the roots, but live and feed in the centers of roots. When the larvae have grown enough, they pupate and undergo complete metamorphosis, emerging as adult beetles in the summer rainy season.

BORROWERS
spiders, invertebrates

KEY FEATURES
- ► holes of ½ inch or more in diverse habitats
- ► half-moon shaped holes
- ► south facing exposure

POSSIBLE BUILDERS
collared lizard (*Crotaphytus collaris*)
whiptails (*Cnemidophorus* spp.)

DESCRIPTION OF HOLES
Some lizards excavate their own holes, but they mostly use burrows of other animals. When they do their own excavating, the holes are about ½ inch in diameter, with a flat bottom and domed top. Lizards prefer a south-facing exposure. In the mornings, they may emerge from their burrows gradually, first sunning their heads, which allows some warmed blood to circulate in their bodies. This brings the animals' temperatures up so they aren't sluggish from the cold and can function efficiently enough to escape predators. Roadrunners often count on lizards being cool and easier to catch in the early mornings.

NATURAL HISTORY OF COLLARED LIZARD
Collared lizards are large, brightly colored, and distinctly patterned. They have big heads and long tails. They favor rocky open areas, canyons, and rocky mountain slopes where they like to lay out and sun on large boulders and rocks. These lizards prey on other lizards, reptiles, and insects, and are very fast runners. Collared lizards can even run bipedally when escaping predators or chasing prey.

Description of Whiptail Holes

Whiptails generally sleep in rodent holes, although they do dig holes while searching for prey, and may sometimes dig their own burrow.

Whiptail and hole

Natural History of Whiptails

Whiptails are long, slender lizards that are very active and fast predators. They live in a variety of habitats, from sandy flats to grasslands and woodlands. Like snakes, whiptails use their tongues to smell with, searching out insects, spiders, scorpions, and some small lizards for food.

Whiptails are unusual in that five out of eight Sonoran Desert species are parthenogenic, meaning the populations consist entirely of females who reproduce by cloning themselves. The offspring are all daughters who are genetically identical to their mothers.

Borrowers
invertebrates

Lizard tracks in sand

KEY FEATURES
- ▶ 1 to 1½ inch hole
- ▶ under bushes or vegetation
- ▶ shallow dens

POSSIBLE BUILDER
cactus mouse (*Peromyscus eremicus*)
pocket mouse (*Perognathus* spp., *Chaetodipus* spp.)
house mouse (*Mus musculus*)

DESCRIPTION OF CACTUS MOUSE HOLE
Holes are less than 1½ inches in diameter and can be in woodpiles, rocky places, old logs or rock crevices, tree roots, or even abandoned verdin nests.

NATURAL HISTORY OF CACTUS MOUSE
Cactus mice are found throughout the desert Southwest in a variety of habitats, including palo verde-saguaro forests, mesquite bosques (forests), grasslands, and riparian areas. They often use the abandoned burrows of other animals, like packrats. They forage for seeds, fruits, and green vegetation. They are a desert species, adapted to getting along on very little water. They may estivate (remain inactive) during the drought and heat of summer.

DESCRIPTION OF POCKET MOUSE HOLES
The 1 to 1½ inch holes are found under bushes or near rocks, and the burrows tend to be shallowly excavated with a spherical nest of grasses in a chamber within the burrow.

NATURAL HISTORY OF POCKET MOUSE
There are several species of pocket mice, four of them

common in the Sonoran Desert. They all have small ears, long tails, and cheek pouches to store and transport seeds.

ROCK POCKET MOUSE
As their name implies, rock pocket mice are found only in rocky habitat in desertscrub. They den in boulder piles, crevices, and rock ledges. They are so well adapted to their rocky environs that many have evolved fur colors that match the color of the rocky substrate they live on. They eat seeds and insects, and are inactive during the winter months.

DESERT POCKET MOUSE
Desert pocket mice prefer open, sandy areas, desert areas with sparse vegetation, and riparian habitats. They eat mostly seeds, including mesquite beans. These mice conserve water by concentrating their urine and sealing their burrows during the day.

Pocket mouse hole

ARIZONA POCKET MOUSE
Arizona pocket mice inhabit sandy open areas and creosote flats. They forage for seeds, especially those of creosote bush. They conserve water with efficient kidneys that concentrate their urine. They also plug burrow holes, which retains humidity in the nest chamber. They fall into a torpor when temperatures become extreme.

BAILEY'S POCKET MOUSE

Bailey's pocket mice, the largest of the pocket mice, are found in flat, open places with creosote and sparse grasses and on bajadas (slopes at the bases of desert mountains) with palo verde and ocotillo. They feed on seeds of various cacti, grasses, and other plants. They are active all year. Bailey's pocket mice are unique in being adapted to eat jojoba nuts, a food that other mice cannot survive on due to its toxic compounds.

Bailey's pocket mouse

DESCRIPTION OF HOUSE MOUSE HOLES

House mouse holes are usually found in and around houses and buildings, or near human activities, like garbage dumps and cultivated fields. The holes are small, less than an inch in diameter.

NATURAL HISTORY OF HOUSE MICE

House mice are not native to the Sonoran Desert or even the United States—they are immigrants from many other parts of the world. Since they are not desert-adapted like our native species, they are restricted to living with or near humans where they can always find a supply of drinking water. This water dependence keeps them from spreading out into desert areas.

BORROWERS

Bumblebees use mouse holes for their colonies.

TRACKS

Pocket mouse

39

KEY FEATURES
➤ about 1½ inch hole
➤ at base of plant or bush
➤ no trails radiating away from hole

POSSIBLE BUILDER
grasshopper mouse (*Onychomys torrida*)

DESCRIPTION OF HOLE
Grasshopper mice build small holes with nearly vertical
4 to 6 inch shafts, which turn to horizontal nest chambers.
The mice are found in desertscrub and grasslands, preferring the more open areas with sparse grasses.

NATURAL HISTORY
Grasshopper mice are fierce little predators. They hunt
lizards, grasshoppers, beetles, scorpions, and even other
mice! They also eat seeds, but they are primarily hunters.

They are very mobile for a rodent, sometimes traveling
up to a mile from their hole to hunt. They defend a much
smaller territory, and they are social, with family units
foraging and hunting together. Male and female grasshopper mice cooperate in raising the young and teaching them
how to hunt. The youngsters need to learn how to bite
the stingers off scorpions before eating them and how to
disable Pinacate beetles, inch-long black insects that
defend themselves by doing a headstand and emitting a
foul-smelling spray from their back ends. The grasshopper
mice grab the beetles, shoving the smelly end in the
ground and biting off the tasty part, leaving a trail of
beetle bottoms embedded in the sand. They kill other mice
by a bite to the back of the head.

Like a tiny wolf pack, grasshopper mice also howl. They stand on the hind legs, throw their heads back and emit high pitched calls to communicate with other family members. It's a very distinctive and eerie call to hear in the desert at night.

Grasshopper mouse

Grasshopper mice are long-lived, some as long as six to eight years, though most probably succumb to predators at a much younger age. Another odd trait in this unusual mouse is that when caught by a predator, the grasshopper mouse flips his bottom end around to throw a runny, very smelly dropping at them. Perhaps this bad smelling insult startles the predator into dropping the mouse, allowing it a chance to escape.

BORROWERS

Spiders, insects, and lizards probably use these holes when abandoned.

KEY FEATURES
► 1½ to 2½ inch hole
► may be under a bush or out in the open
► many holes in an area
► may be a mound of dirt at hole

POSSIBLE BUILDER
round-tailed ground squirrel (*Spermophilus tereticaudus*)

DESCRIPTION OF HOLE
Round-tails occupy much the same habitat as jackrabbits—
open flat areas with sandy or silty alluvial soils. There are
usually quite a number of round-tailed ground squirrel
holes around the base of a bush or out in the open, though
all the holes may be only one house. Round-tails throw out
a fan of dirt at the entrance hole as they excavate, making
a mound a couple of inches high. Some of the other holes
that have been in use for a longer time will be flat. There
are often many shallow exploration holes nearby where
the squirrels have dug for seeds.

NATURAL HISTORY
Round-tails resemble miniature prairie dogs and though
they aren't, they do share some traits. Like prairie dogs,
they are social and colonial, and in areas of good habitat
there may be a few dozen families. They dig extensive tunnel networks with many escape routes and various openings
leading down to the 3 foot deep nest chambers. Early winter months are spent underground in their burrows; they
emerge in late January or February to feed and fatten up on
the new spring vegetation. They are primarily vegetarians,
eating seeds, green vegetation, cactus, cactus flowers and

fruit, mesquite buds and leaves, and ocotillo flowers. They can be seen clambering about in mesquite trees gathering new buds and leaves in spring. They also eat carrion and road kills, even other ground squirrels. You can sometimes see one dragging a small carcass off the road to eat.

The most delightful time to watch round-tailed ground squirrels is early morning in May and early June. The mother squirrel emerges first, checks the area for predators, yawns, and stretches, then calls the youngsters, who come spilling out of the burrow to begin wrestling and playing, interspersed with bouts of feeding. Being at the bottom of the food chain, round-tails often stand on their hind legs to watch for hawks, snakes, coyotes, foxes, badgers, and their many other predators. On spotting danger, one will call a chirp-like "peeps" to alert the others, and they all disappear down the burrows.

These squirrels are diurnal, with a very relaxed lifestyle. Most activity occurs from early morning to about noon, when they retire for a siesta. Another brief period of activity occurs in late afternoon. They sometimes seal the burrow entrance with dirt at night to prevent snakes from visiting.

Round-tails seldom get to drink water, depending on green vegetation and cactus for moisture; therefore they usually estivate (remain inactive or dormant) for a few weeks during the drought of summer until the rains come bringing new vegetation to eat.

COMMENSAL USERS AND BORROWERS
Scorpions are known to live in ground squirrel burrows. Burrowing owls may enlarge and use an abandoned ground squirrel house; snakes, lizards, spiders, and invertebrates all use these burrows.

TRACK

3/4"

Ground squirrel

KEY FEATURES
- ▶ hole near bush or cactus or among rocks
- ▶ no mound of dirt at hole
- ▶ 2 to 2½ inch diameter holes

POSSIBLE BUILDER
Harris' antelope squirrel (*Ammospermophilus harrisii*)

DESCRIPTION OF HOLE
The Harris' antelope squirrel's burrow entrance is typically found in sheltered spots—in cactus patches, under bushes, or among rocks—but Harris' antelope squirrel and round-tailed ground squirrel ranges overlap in some areas so their holes might be confused with one another. The round-tails' holes are more often out in the open, in social colonies, whereas the Harris' squirrel is solitary and only one burrow with several entrance holes is found in an area. Bits and pieces of cactus fruit are often left lying nearby where the Harris' antelope squirrel has been feeding.

NATURAL HISTORY
The Harris' antelope squirrels are often mistaken for chipmunks because of the white stripe on their sides, but chipmunks have white stripes on the face as well as on the sides, and they live in the higher elevation forests, while the antelope squirrels live in rocky desert areas.

Harris' antelope squirrels are diurnal and active year round, unlike the round-tailed ground squirrels who hibernate and estivate (remain inactive or dormant).

Harris' antelope squirrel hole

Harris' antelope squirrels feed not so much on green vegetation as on seeds, mesquite beans, palo verde seeds, fruits
of prickly pear, barrel cactus, and cholla, as well as insects
and an occasional mouse. They survive without drinking
much water, deriving what they need from their food.

They are very active little creatures, often running
about with their bushy tails arched over their backs,
foraging even when it is very hot. The tail shades the
animal, keeping it cooler. When the antelope squirrel
begins to get overheated it runs into its burrow, where it
spread-eagles itself on the cool, moist earth and dumps
heat from its body to the soil. Once cooled the little
squirrel is back on the surface again foraging. This pattern
may be repeated many times a day.

When a Harris' antelope squirrel detects a predator, it
often stands on its hind legs to get a better view, then gives
a warning sound that is often mistaken for a bird's trilling
call, before dashing to safety.

BORROWERS
Snakes, Gila monsters and other lizards, spiders, and
invertebrates may use a squirrel hole.

KEY FEATURES
- round hole about 3 to 5 inches at the base of a large mound of sticks, cactus joints, and debris
- near the base of prickly pear, mesquite, cholla, or rock crevice

POSSIBLE BUILDER
white throated wood rat (packrat) (*Neotoma albigula*)

DESCRIPTION OF HOLE
Although a packrat house appears on the outside to be a messy pile of sticks, twigs, cactus joints, animal dung, and assorted debris, the inside is structured with various tunnels and chambers. The houses are often built within

Packrat house

a prickly pear cactus patch, at the base of a cholla or mesquite tree, or in a rocky crevice. The pile of debris can be 8 feet or more wide, and 2 to 3 feet high. At least one or two entrance holes are visible at the base of the pile, allowing the rodent a quick escape out the back door if snakes or other predators come in the front. Often, there are obvious runways leading to and from the house.

Packrat

NATURAL HISTORY

Wood rats (packrats) live throughout the desert Southwest in a variety of habitats, from chaparral to desert grasslands to ponderosa pine forests; they are common in palo verde-saguaro forests. Packrats are solitary animals, with only one rodent per house, unless it is a female with offspring. Females are more sedentary than males and usually occupy the best house sites, which often are passed on to one of the owner's daughters.

The pile of sticks, cactus parts, and debris in a house not only protects the packrat from predators, but also helps to insulate the nest, which is a small chamber lined with grasses only a few inches under the ground surface. There the packrat sleeps and raises its family. The packrat is always adding to the house, hauling large sticks up to 2 feet long, and even cholla joints, which it carries in its mouth! Chambers and tunnels are also extended, creating space for food storage, or escape routes.

When night brings cooler temperatures and higher humidity, packrats emerge to forage for mesquite beans, cholla buds and fruit, prickly pear, palo verde seeds, and other plant material. They can survive without water, deriving the moisture they need from the cactus they eat, but in the lowest desert areas they can only live where there are enough succulents, especially cholla, to sustain them.

BORROWERS, COMMENSAL USERS

Packrat houses are the "bed and breakfasts" of the desert community, with many other creatures taking advantage of the rodents' (often unwilling) hospitality. Snakes not only find a meal (the packrat), but also a nice place to sleep out of the heat. Crickets, spiders, centipedes, lizards, Gila monsters, and desert tortoises may also take refuge in a packrat's house.

The infamous conenose bugs (kissing bugs) also live in packrat houses, sucking blood from their rodent hosts. Funnel web spiders often use the outside of the house as a

TRACKS

Packrat

handy place to spin their webs. Occasionally javelinas come along and tear the house apart to steal the wood rat's cache of mesquite beans or palo verde seeds.

KEY FEATURES
- ► hole about 4 inches in diameter
- ► can be among rocks and boulders
- ► can be a large mound of dirt at entrance

POSSIBLE BUILDER
rock squirrel (*Spermophilus variegatus*)

DESCRIPTION OF HOLE
Rock squirrels are great excavators, digging large, perfectly round holes in cutbanks, near or between rocks, under tree roots and sometimes under a mesquite tree. There can be a large mound of dirt thrown out from the hole, but in rocky places this doesn't always show. Food scraps like hollowed out prickly pear fruits or pieces of barrel cactus fruit are found in the vicinity of the hole.

NATURAL HISTORY
Rock squirrels may look like tree squirrels but they're not, preferring to live in underground burrows, although they can climb trees perfectly well. They are the largest of our ground squirrels, weighing about 1½ pounds. Rock squirrels are found throughout the desert Southwest in a wide variety of habitats, including desertscrub and any place where there are rocky outcrops, boulder piles, or canyon walls with niches. They are very adaptable, and houses and old buildings, tree roots, and many other sites may also serve as shelters.

Rock squirrels are omnivores, feeding on a variety of fruits, including prickly pear fruit, seeds, mesquite beans, palo verde seeds, berries, insects, birds, and carrion. During the late summer months rock squirrels are often seen with red stains around their mouths. This isn't blood but juice from prickly pear fruit. These squirrels store food for winter use, when they remain in their dens. Biologists are not certain about whether they actually hibernate, since they do come out on some warm, sunny winter days.

Rock squirrel

Rock squirrels are diurnal, and can usually be seen in the mornings sitting and sunning themselves on some high rocky perch with a good view. If they spot a roadrunner, hawk, coyote, or other predator they repeatedly give a sharp whistle-like warning call. When rock squirrels encounter snakes, they stamp their feet while waving their tails side to side and attempting to push sand or dirt at the snake's face with their front paws.

BORROWERS
Many snakes, reptiles, and other animals will use a rock squirrel's abode. A species of conenose bug (kissing bug) also inhabits rock squirrel houses.

TRACKS

1¼"

Rock squirrel

KEY FEATURES
 ► large mounds
 ► as many as 12 tall, oval entrance holes
 ► built in open spaces
 ► trails or runways leading from mound

POSSIBLE BUILDERS
banner-tailed kangaroo rat (*Dipodomys spectabilis*)
Merriam's kangaroo rat (*Dipodomys merriami*)

DESCRIPTION OF HOLE
The banner-tailed kangaroo rat digs an extensive system of
tunnels, kicking the dirt out into large mounds that look
like they should belong to a prairie dog. The mound can
be 3 or 4 feet high and anywhere from 5 to 15 feet in
diameter. Entrance holes are about 6 inches high. Tracks
and tail drag marks might be seen on the runways near the
mound, but droppings are usually not seen.

One half the size of the banner-tails, Merriam's kangaroo rats construct much smaller burrow systems, usually
near a creosote bush or mesquite tree, with entrance holes
about 3 inches high. They are found in sandy soils in
desertscrub where grasses are interspersed with mesquite,
creosote, and cacti.

NATURAL HISTORY
Banner-tailed kangaroo rats, the largest of the kangaroo
rats, reside in open desert scrub, creosote flats, sandy
places, and open grasslands. They like a sparse covering
of grass interspersed with a few mesquite trees, catclaw,
and cactus. Their tunnel systems contain many rooms for
food storage, nest chambers, and a number of escape

51

*Kangaroo rat holes
at the base of a creosote bush*

routes. The surface mounds grow larger as the kangaroo rat
digs additional tunnels. Kangaroo rats are solitary, with
only one rodent per mound. They defend a territory and
often fight when they encounter each other.

Kangaroo rats are vegetarians, subsisting primarily on
a diet of grass seeds and mesquite beans. They forage at
night, stuffing seeds in their cheek pouches to carry back
to the burrow, where they store the seeds for later use.

Merriam's kangaroo rat is the most common kangaroo
rat in the Sonoran Desert area. They feed on seeds,
especially seeds of grasses, and take some insects and
vegetation, but they don't store food underground in the
burrows as the banner-tail does. They prefer to bury seeds
just under surface in various scattered caches. They are
active year round, although they don't tolerate extremes
of heat or cold very well, usually retiring underground to
escape when conditions are unsuitable.

Kangaroo rats are well adapted to their arid lifestyle.
They seldom drink, as they are able to obtain water as a

by-product of metabolizing the seeds they eat. During the day while they are sleeping, kangaroo rats plug their burrow holes, which conserves humidity and reduces heat. Stored seeds in the burrow absorb up to 30% more moisture from the humidity in the burrow, providing the rat with additional moisture. Kangaroo rats can reabsorb water from their efficient kidneys, which concentrate the

Merriam's kangaroo rat

urine to a very viscous consistency, with a high uric acid content. Their nasal passages are designed to reabsorb moisture from the breath as it is exhaled, allowing this little creature to not just survive, but thrive in this arid environment.

Kangaroo rats are also adapted to bathing without water. They take sand baths, which help absorb excess oils in the fur, keeping them shiny and clean.

Kangaroo rats are preyed on by owls, snakes, foxes, badgers, and coyotes. With so many predators, the kangaroo rats have evolved exceptionally keen hearing, allowing them to hear snakes moving or an owl swooping down on them.

The name "kangaroo rat" comes from the rodent's habit of hopping or traveling bipedally on its large hind feet. Bones in the feet are fused for extra strength, allowing the kangaroo rat to jump 10 feet in a bound!

BORROWERS
Burrowing owls might use a banner-tailed kangaroo rat mound.

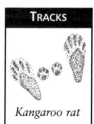

TRACKS

Kangaroo rat

KEY FEATURES
► 7 to 12 inches, tall oval shape
► in sandy flat areas, desert grassland
► multiple entrances

POSSIBLE BUILDER
kit fox (*Vulpes macrotus*)

DESCRIPTION OF HOLE
Kit fox dens are most common in flat, open areas with little vegetation, perhaps sparse grasses and a few bushes. They often appropriate a badger digging or other hole for their own house. There is a good-sized mound of dirt outside the den entrance, and usually 2 and sometimes up to 10 entrances in very extensive dens. Trails are evident leading to and from the den area. In spring, bits of fur, feathers, food scraps, and scat littering the site indicate an active den with pups.

NATURAL HISTORY
Kit foxes, weighing only 4 to 5 pounds and standing about 1 foot tall, are the smallest members of the canine tribe. They live in arid, flat regions with diggable soils, such as creosote flats, desertscrub, farmland, and grassland. A nocturnal hunter, kit foxes prey mainly on kangaroo rats, who also prefer the same flat, open habitat. Other food items include cottontails, jackrabbits, ground squirrels, mice, insects like grasshoppers and crickets, the occasional lizard or bird, plant material, and carrion. They can survive without free water, obtaining water from their prey, and so can live in the most arid areas.

Kit fox at its den

Kit foxes are unusual in being the only canine to use dens year round. Resting underground during the heat of day probably helps them survive the aridity and heat of their desert habitat. During July through September they are solitary, with individuals using small dens that they change frequently, sometimes four or five times a month. In the fall female foxes move into larger family dens, cleaning and renovating them in preparation for the pups. The males join them later. Kit foxes do not mate for life, and may have a different partner each season. The pups (about three to five) are born in February and March, and both parents feed the young, primarily kangaroo rats, for about four to five months. A kit fox might spend its life within a 1 or 2 square mile area. Because they change dens frequently there may be quite a few den holes in that area, making it look like there is a larger population of the foxes than there really is.

TRACK

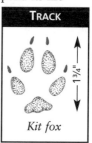

1 3/4"

Kit fox

BORROWERS
Burrowing owls often use kit fox dens.

KEY FEATURES
- ► oval shape about 7 inches high by 12 inches wide
- ► wide fan of dirt outside hole
- ► many holes in an area

POSSIBLE BUILDER
badger (*Taxidea taxus*)

DESCRIPTION OF HOLE
Badgers are prodigious diggers, and usually many holes are found wherever badgers are active. The holes are badger-shaped, low and wide, about 12 inches or so wide by 7 or 8 inches high. The badgers throw out a 4 to 6 foot wide fan of dirt at the entrance to their holes. There is usually no evidence of food scraps or scats around the entrances.

NATURAL HISTORY
Badgers are a member of the weasel clan, a whole family known for its strength, tenacity, and ferocity. Most animals think twice before arguing with a badger, though the badger only weighs 15 to 25 pounds. It has a loose, heavy hide with thick fur. When a dog or other inexperienced would-be attacker tries to bite a badger, they find the tables turned quickly, as the badger twists around in its hide and bites and slashes at the attacker-turned-victim.

They are nocturnal hunters that dig for their dinner. Armed with 12 inch long claws on their powerful front feet, badgers can dig rodents out of their burrows in seconds. Badgers possess a transparent nictitating membrane that covers and protects their eyes while the badgers dig and dirt is flying. They occasionally take fox or coyote puppies from their dens, but most often eat gophers, kangaroo rats, packrats, ground squirrels, prairie dogs, rattlesnakes, insects, lizards, birds, eggs, rabbits, and carrion. Coyotes have been known to follow badgers as they hunt, waiting to take advantage of rodents escaping out the back door as the badger digs up the front door, though there does not seem to be much advantage to the badger in this arrangement.

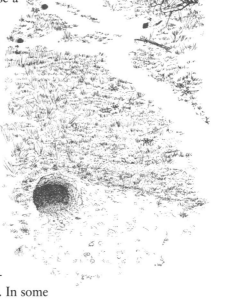

Badgers don't use a regular den site, simply retiring for the day into one of the many burrows they dug out while hunting during the night. Badgers live in the same habitats that kit fox and kangaroo rats prefer—open, sandy flat areas with easily diggable soil, like alluvial fans, creosote flats, farmland, and grassland. In some urban areas they even use golf courses.

Hole dug by badger

Badgers are solitary and seldom seen together, except during the breeding season of July and August. As might be expected from their temperament, badger courtship is brief, both parties going their separate ways after mating.

Because of delayed implantation the two to five babies are not born until February or March. The female badger enlarges one of the many holes in her territory for a maternity den. Young badgers only stay with the mother for three months or so, then are off on their own. Many end up as road kills in late summer and fall when they disperse from their dens.

Badger

Badger populations in Arizona have declined as ranchers have attempted to eradicate them from rangeland, fearing their horses might break a leg falling into a badger hole. Badgers are also adversely affected when prairie dogs and other prey animals are poisoned.

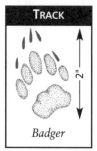

Signs of badger activity are predominantly the many diggings and holes. The tracks are distinctive, toed-in, and with the long claws showing. Scats are not usually found.

BORROWERS
Burrowing owls, coyotes, kit foxes, and rabbits use badger holes.

KEY FEATURES
- ▸ about 12 to 24 inches, taller than wide
- ▸ often on a hillside or bank of a wash
- ▸ may be more than one den in an area
- ▸ evidence of trampled vegetation or trails

POSSIBLE BUILDER
coyote (*Canis latrans*)

DESCRIPTION OF HOLE
Coyotes only use dens when whelping and raising pups. They are extremely secretive about den locations, which are rarely found by people. Coyotes may dig their own dens, but often modify an existing burrow or den of another animal like a badger or even a packrat. The front entrance may be fairly visible with a lot of dirt piled around a large hole. A tunnel then leads to a larger chamber, sometimes with a second, more concealed entrance. Plenty of other signs of coyote activity should be evident, like food remains, tracks, scent posts, and scats.

NATURAL HISTORY
Coyotes are found throughout the desert Southwest. Opportunistic eaters, the coyote will feed on anything—meat, carrion, fruit, seeds, and plant material. Although they hunt small animals like rodents, rabbits, snakes, and birds, they also scavenge, eating road kills or leftovers from a mountain lion kill. Desert coyotes weigh only about 15 to 25 pounds; in colder climates they are usually heavier.

Coyotes vary in temperament; some are solitary, but most are social creatures that live in small family groups, with both parents helping to feed and raise the pups.

*Coyote pups
in a den*

Sometimes yearling pups may stay with the parent coyotes through the first winter to help raise the new family the next spring. These social groups may also hunt cooperatively. They vocalize (or sing) for a variety of reasons: to communicate with separated members of the family, to tell neighboring packs where they are, and sometimes it seems they howl and yip just to celebrate life.

Within the larger hunting range is a central core area where various den sites are located. Coyotes scent mark and defend this area. A coyote urinates on a plant or rock, then scrapes with his hind feet to leave both a visual and a scent marker. Scats are also used to advertise that the area is occupied. Coyote scats vary in shape, size, and composition depending on what the animals ate. Sometimes the scat will be full of javelina fur or snake scales, other times saguaro fruit seeds or mesquite beans. Coyotes can't seem to pass by any other animal's scat without commenting on it by leaving their own dropping on top of the other.

If a den was successful (that is, if the pups survived) it will probably be used again the following season. There are usually several dens in an area, and the pups may be moved several times. If people disturb a coyote den it is promptly abandoned and the pups are moved to a safer spot. Coyotes may also change dens to escape fleas, ticks, or other parasites. Once in a while dens are constructed above ground in brush thickets or heavy vegetation.

BORROWERS

Skunks, snakes, spiders, and invertebrates will use coyote dens. Sometimes as it collapses after disuse, a packrat may move in and refurbish the hole, bringing in debris to fill the entrance.

TRACK

2½"

Coyote

DEPRESSIONS

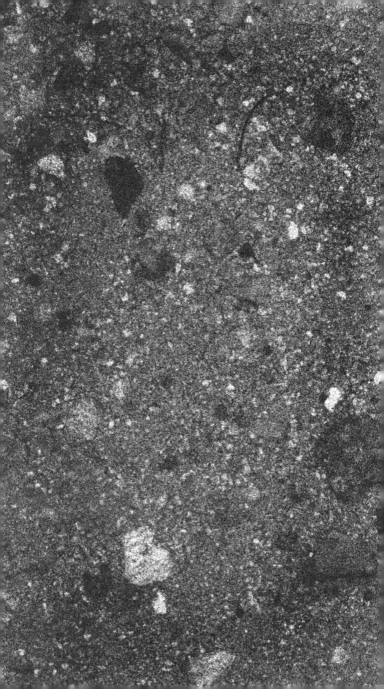

KEY FEATURES
- ► conical shaped depression in ground
- ► found in fine dry soil or sand
- ► ½ to 2 inches

POSSIBLE BUILDER
antlion (Myrmeleontidae family)

DESCRIPTION OF DEPRESSION
Antlion larvae construct a conical depression in sand or fine soil to trap ants and other insects for food. There are usually a number of antlion holes clustered in a suitable area. They vary in size from ½ inch to about 2 inches depending on the age and size of the larvae. Sometimes the twisting, canal-shaped tracks of the larvae are evident as they move to new hunting spots.

NATURAL HISTORY
Adult antlions are winged insects that look like large gray damselflies and are about 1½ inches long. They are nocturnal predators often seen around lights at night, but they seem poor fliers and are timid for predators.

The larval form of the antlion looks like a gray, fuzzy seed with large jaws and is far more impressive than the adult in its habits. The predacious larva digs a conical pit in the ground where it waits, hidden at the bottom, for unwary ants or other insects to fall into the trap. As an ant struggles to gain its footing in the steep-sided, loose sand, the antlion throws sprays of sand up, causing the prey to lose traction and slide to the bottom. The antlion, with its large mouthparts, then pierces the ant and injects a

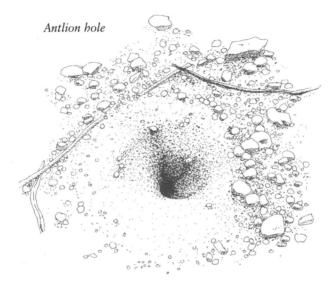

Antlion hole

digestive enzyme. The ant is then pulled under the sand, where the ant lion can suck out the juices undisturbed.

Because antlions are sit-and-wait hunters, depending on the chance of an ant passing by and falling into the trap, meals are unpredictable; it therefore may take up to two years for the antlion larva to get enough nutrition to grow to sufficient size to pupate into an adult. The antlion larva builds its cocoon in the sand at the bottom of its hole, overwinters, and emerges as a flying adult in the early summer. If hunting is poor in an area, the larva might abandon its trap and move to a new location, though usually not more than a few feet away.

Antlion larvae are found anywhere there is fine dry soil and a supply of ants.

BORROWERS
none known

KEY FEATURES
- ► round or oval depression in ground
- ► up to 7 inches in diameter
- ► in washes, banks of streams, dry pools

POSSIBLE BUILDERS
Sonoran Desert toad (*Bufo alvarius*)
Couch's spadefoot (*Scaphiopus couchi*)

DESCRIPTION OF DEPRESSIONS
Depressions in sandy washes or banks are made by toads as they burrow into the ground to bury themselves. The hole fills in above the toads as they burrow deeper, so the holes and resulting depressions are only obvious while the toads are actually burying themselves. This usually happens toward the end of the summer rainy season. Depressions are anywhere from a few inches to 6 or 7 inches in diameter, depending on the size of the toad.

NATURAL HISTORY OF THE SONORAN DESERT TOAD
The largest toad native to the United States, the Sonoran Desert toad is an impressive sight at up to 6 or 7 inches in length. They're often found near permanent water, streams, washes, and canyons, but also in drier desert areas. Toads are more able to tolerate being away from water than frogs, and they may hide in animal burrows during the heat of the day to avoid dessication.

Sonoran Desert toads emerge in summer, spending their nights hunting insects and small animals. These toads have large parotoid glands toward the backs of their heads that secrete a very toxic poison. It is an effective defense against predators. If a dog or coyote mouths a toad, it immediately begins frothing or salivating and staggering about, and may even become paralyzed. Occasionally the poison can be fatal, but most animals do recover.

Sonoran Desert toads breed during the summer rainy season, seeking out deeper pools that will last longer, since their tadpoles can take two months or more to grow and metamorphose into toadlets.

Natural History of Couch's Spadefoot

In a land full of amazing animal adaptations, the spadefoot is right at the top of the list.

They sleep for most of the year until the first heavy downpour of the summer rainy season causes them to emerge and begin their two or three months of activity. The vibration and sound of the rain stimulates them to dig

Emerging Couch's spadefoot

their way to the surface where they congregate in the temporary rain pools in desert washes and canyons, irrigation canals, and ponds. The loud, sheeplike bleating calls of the males are a familiar sound to those who live out in the desert. Because the pools and rains are temporary and unpredictable, there is no time to waste. There is a frenzy of calling, breeding, and egg laying especially on the first night they emerge. In the morning, pools are filled with eggs that hatch into tadpoles, then race to metamorphose into toadlets before the pools dry up. They can go from egg to toadlet in 14 days!

The adult spadefoots are insectivores and especially like termites, one of the most nutritious insects in the desert. The termites are also keyed into the first summer rain, and send out their mating flights the same night the spadefoots emerge. The spadefoots feast on the termites and need only fill their stomachs twice to obtain enough nutrition to survive until the next year's rainy season. They spend the days resting in burrows of ground squirrels, gophers, or other animals, or they sometimes dig their own retreats.

At the end of the rainy season, the spadefoots bury themselves in dry washes or similar places by working their way backwards into the ground. They dig with their hind feet, which are equipped with hard keratinous spade-like pads (hence the name spadefoot) until they bury themselves. It isn't known how deep the animals burrow. They may live for 10 or more years, although they face new challenges they are not adapted for, such as being run over by cars on rainy nights.

BORROWERS
Because no real hole is left, there are no borrowers.

KEY FEATURES
- ► shallow forms
- ► a short tunnel or hollow under a bush, covered by grasses and vegetation
- ► about 5 by 7 inches

Possible Builder
desert cottontail rabbit (*Sylvilagus audubonii*)

Description of Depression
Cottontail rabbit forms may vary from a hidden spot like a short hollow space beneath a covering of grasses and weeds to a bare shady spot beneath a shrub, tree, or cactus. They also use the abandoned burrows of ground squirrels, skunks, badgers, or other animals.

Cottontail rabbit form

About the only holes rabbits actually dig themselves are shallow ones around 4 inches deep by 5 inches wide and 7 inches long, as a nest for newborn babies. These are lined with grasses and the mother rabbit's fur, then covered over with grasses to hide the newborn rabbits.

Desert cottontail

NATURAL HISTORY

The desert cottontail is found throughout the desert Southwest, including grasslands, but they prefer the more thickly vegetated areas with lots of hiding places. Although primarily nocturnal, these rabbits are commonly seen during the morning and evening hours. During the heat of day they retire to "forms"—shaded brushy spots, or brush piles—to rest.

Cottontails are herbivores, feeding on a wide variety of green plants, grasses, and other broadleaf flowering plants. They also use prickly pear cactus as a source of moisture.

Rabbits can survive on water from the plants they eat, but if free water is available they drink readily.

Desert cottontails breed throughout the spring and summer months, and rabbit courtship is a very energetic affair, with lots of chases, charges, leaping over each other, and spraying each other with urine. About a month after mating, the female gives birth to three or four babies, which are hidden in the nest most of the time. She returns only a few times each night to nurse them. Although born blind and unfurred, the little rabbits are able to leave the nest after only a few weeks. When they are very young, cottontails don't venture far at all, staying close to the safety of a bush or other shelter.

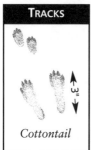

TRACKS

↑ 3" ↓

Cottontail

Cottontails are social creatures and sometimes groups of them are seen together at night. These gathering places, often on trails or in washes, can be recognized by the many pellet droppings and urine spots.

BORROWERS
none known

KEY FEATURES
- ► shallow scrape under a bush or cactus
- ► about 6 inches by 12 inches

POSSIBLE BUILDERS
black-tailed jackrabbit (*Lepus californicus*)
antelope jackrabbit (*Lepus alleni*)

DESCRIPTION OF DEPRESSION
A jackrabbit form, or resting spot, is really only a bare spot in the shade or a very shallow depression next to a clump of plants or under a mesquite, cholla, or other plant.

NATURAL HISTORY
Jackrabbits are creatures of the dry open areas of the desert Southwest, and are found in creosote flats, grassland, and farmland, although they can also be seen in desert upland habitats. They can easily be distinguished from the cottontails by their much larger size (up to 8 or 10 pounds), and huge ears. Jackrabbits are members of the hare family. The antelope jack is the largest hare in the United States, with white tipped ears and a patch of white fur on the sides that can be flashed much like a pronghorn antelope does when fleeing danger. The black-tailed jackrabbit is smaller and has black-tipped ears.

Jackrabbits are mostly nocturnal and crepuscular (active at dusk and dawn), resting in their forms during the heat of the day. The form may be a shallow scrape near a clump of grass or simply a patch of shade under a mesquite or beside a cactus. When they sense danger such as a predator lurking nearby, they stand on their hind legs to get a better view of the situation, turning the large ears to catch any sound. Jackrabbit eyes are placed high and toward the back of their heads allowing them to see in nearly 360 degrees with only a slight turn of their heads. If a coyote or other predator is nearby, jacks crouch down and freeze, with ears lowered, preferring not to run unless absolutely necessary. If they have to run, the jacks sail across the desert in great leaps of 15 feet or more, occasionally leaping quite high to catch a glimpse of where the predator is. They have been known to run at 35 miles per hour.

Jacks are herbivores, feeding mostly on grasses, mesquite, prickly pear, acacias, palo verde, and snakeweed. They can survive in very dry areas, getting moisture from plants and prickly pear cactus, but they must conserve all the water they can by restricting their activities to the cooler and more humid hours.

Jackrabbits breed throughout the year. Like the rabbits, courtship is a matter of charges, chases, and leaping over each other. After a six-week gestation period, one or two baby jacks are born. Unlike cottontails, jackrabbit babies

TRACKS

6"

Jackrabbit

are precocial; they are born fully furred and with their eyes open. The young jackrabbits may stay with the mother for several months.

Jacks are fairly social and large groups of them gather, especially on moonlit nights.

BORROWERS
none known

KEY FEATURES
- ▶ shallow circular depression, usually with a ridge of soil around edges
- ▶ about 7 to 9 inches in diameter, depending on size of snake
- ▶ depression usually in fine soil, free of rocks or sticks

POSSIBLE BUILDER
rattlesnake (*Crotalus* spp.)

DESCRIPTION OF DEPRESSION
Rattlesnakes make a resting form that is a shallow round or oval depression by coiling up and pushing debris out with their heavy bodies. These resting forms can be found out in the open in washes, on trails, or at the base of vegetation. If the form is very fresh (the edges are crisp and sharp, no evidence of bird or rodent tracks in the form), the snake may not be too far away. If the soil is soft the snake may leave a track as it moves away from the form.

NATURAL HISTORY
Rattlesnakes occur in all habitats within the desert Southwest, with the western diamondback being the largest and one of the most common species. Snakes are ectotherms, controlling their body temperature externally by moving in and out of the sun and shade. In the Sonoran Desert, they are most often found above ground during the warmer months of the year, although they occasionally sun themselves on a warm winter day. They are most active during the cooler hours of morning and evening, but with the intense heat of summer, they retire to cooler, shaded

areas for the day, emerging when night brings relief. Rattlesnakes caught out in the summer midday sun of the Sonoran Desert will die of overheating in only a few minutes.

Rattlesnakes are usually sit-and-wait hunters, curling up along a trail or area that is likely to have rodent, bird, or rabbit activity and waiting for some unwary passerby. They also like to sit on rocks near water holes or shallow

Blacktail rattlesnake

streams waiting for prey, especially birds, to come to drink. They often hide under vegetation, in brush piles, among rocky outcrops and crevices, and in or near packrat houses and other rodent burrows. Rattlesnakes sit unmoving for hours, relying on their cryptic coloration for camouflage. Most people have walked by numerous snakes while out hiking and never known it.

Rattlesnake vision is short range, up to about 10 feet, and geared to movement, but they are also equipped with a heat-sensing loreal pit on either side of the face that can detect even slight variations in temperature up to a foot away. This heat information is processed in the visual cortex of the brain, allowing the snake to "see" in heat pictures, making them very accurate in striking, even at night. A rattlesnake does not strike indiscriminately, and usually won't strike an animal too big for it to eat, unless in self-defense when the snake feels threatened or harassed.

Rattlesnakes use their forked tongues to smell. As the tongue flicks out it picks up scent particles, which are then relayed to the Jacobsen's organs in the roof of the mouth. If a prey animal manages to get away after being envenomated by a rattlesnake, the snake can easily follow the scent trail of the victim and then simply wait for the venom to work. Occasionally the snake loses track of its prey and may hunt for a few hours trying to find it again. The victim may escape the snake only to die from the venom anyway.

It is a fallacy that rattlesnakes must coil to strike—they can bite from any position. Coiling in defense probably allows the snake to minimize the amount of exposed and unprotected body and lets it readily face a predator that doesn't stand still. Coiling also allows the snake to maximize the distance and perhaps the speed of its strike.

BORROWERS
Birds sometimes adopt snake resting forms to use as dust baths.

KEY FEATURES
- ▸ shallow oval with a raised ridge around it
- ▸ up to 12 inches in diameter, 1-3 inches deep
- ▸ found near vegetation that may cast shade on the depression

POSSIBLE BUILDER
desert tortoise (*Gopherus agassizii*)

DESCRIPTION OF DEPRESSION
The "pallets" or resting spots of desert tortoises resemble the outline of a tortoise. They are found under various kinds of vegetation, from palo verdes to clumps of grass that cast shade, but are almost never in the open. To make them, tortoises scrape with their front feet to clear a spot and then settle themselves into the pallets, forming a ridge of soil around themselves. Pallets are used in September and October (possibly in spring as well), once the heat of summer has broken and the need to hide underground has passed. Tortoises remain well concealed as they rest, basking in the warmth but not directly in the sun. They may spend hours or even a few days resting in these pallets. Scats may be found nearby.

NATURAL HISTORY
The desert tortoise, though a member of the turtle family, is truly a terrestrial animal, so well adapted to dry land that it will drown if it falls into deep water. In the Sonoran Desert they are found most commonly in the palo verde-saguaro forest, although they also occur in the lower desert and some grassland habitats. Tortoises prefer rocky, hilly terrain over low flat areas. Like little four-wheel drive

vehicles, tortoises clamber slowly about, negotiating steep slopes simply by staying in first gear. They are tied to their home range, spending their lives of 50 or more years in an area of just a few miles, where they know how to find water and food in each season, as well as dens, burrows, and shelter sites. Population densities vary throughout their habitat, but these populations tend to be isolated from each other and are thus more vulnerable to being wiped out by disease, habitat loss, or depredation.

Desert tortoise

In southern Arizona, tortoises hibernate during the winter in underground dens or rock shelters. These gentle reptiles emerge from their dens and become active in the milder temperatures of spring and fall, and only during the cooler hours of morning and evening in the summer.

Tortoises are herbivores, foraging on over 100 species of food plants in the Sonoran Desert, especially the spring wildflowers, janusia, prickly pear cactus fruits, and grasses. Desert tortoises can absorb some moisture from the vegetation they eat, but they still need to drink water when they can, often seeking out puddles during the summer rainy season. Tortoises have a large urinary bladder which can store water to see it through times of drought. When a tortoise is frightened by a predator or a person, it may release the stored water in its bladder, leaving it to slowly die of dehydration if it cannot replace the fluids.

Male tortoises are pugnacious, often fighting each other in pushing matches, each trying to overturn the other to claim mating opportunities. If the overturned male cannot right himself, he will die.

As with most long-lived animals, tortoises are slow to reach sexual maturity, which occurs at around 8 to 15 years. They can mate at any time, because the females are able to retain viable sperm for more than a year. The female tortoise then lays an average of four to nine eggs in July, just in time for the summer rains. The 2 inch long babies hatch in September or October, but very few survive to adulthood. If the little tortoises can survive their first five years and are not adversely impacted by humans or disease, they stand a good chance of surviving to a ripe old age.

Evidence of tortoises in an area are scats, half-moon-shaped burrows, or tracks, usually only seen in sandy or dusty soil such as on trails or in washes.

COMMENTS
See also the Borrowed/Modified Shelters section for information on tortoise burrows.

BORROWERS
None known for tortoise pallets, though other animals do use tortoise burrows.

KEY FEATURES
- ➤ large but shallow depressions, about 24 by 40 inches
- ➤ loose, disturbed soil
- ➤ under trees or in thick brush
- ➤ many scats around area

POSSIBLE BUILDERS
javelina (collared peccary) (*Tayassu tajacu*)

DESCRIPTION OF DEPRESSION

Javelina beds are usually found along and above the banks of washes, in areas of thick vegetation, typically mesquite, palo verde, hackberry, catclaw, or jojoba. The beds vary in size from space enough for a few animals (about 24 by 40 inches), to large beds with room enough for the whole herd (about 4 feet by 7 or 8 feet or more). If there is only enough shade under a tree for two or three javelinas then there will be several beds under other nearby trees. These beds show evidence of disturbed, kicked up soil, and 5sometimes loose hairs left by the javelina. There may also be piles of scat around the bed ground or on trails leading to the bedding area. Javelinas are the only large mammal to leave many scats at a bed ground. Other evidence may include bits and pieces of chewed prickly pear and hoof prints.

NATURAL HISTORY

Javelinas are social creatures, living in herds of 2 to 20 animals, with the usual number between 8 and 12. They inhabit desertscrub or desert grassland areas with mixed shrubs and cacti, but use other habitats as well. Javelinas defend territories of about 800 acres. Within the home range are trails leading to various bed grounds, water-holes, and feeding areas. Javelinas are primarily herbivores, dining on flowering plants, roots, tubers, grasses, mesquite beans, seeds, cactus fruits, agave, and prickly pear cactus, which is a staple of javelina diet. In the Sonoran Desert, javelinas are not usually found in areas that lack sufficient patches of prickly pear. Javelinas will also eat an occasional

Javelina bed

dead bird or rodent.

Both males and females are equipped with large canine teeth that are used primarily for defense. When irritated or showing aggression, javelinas snap their teeth together rapidly, making a popping or clacking noise. They also make a variety of other sounds—woofing, grunting, barking, growling, and squealing (especially the younger ones). Javelinas have poor vision, relying instead on their hearing and sense of smell. They have scent glands on their backs near their rumps that secrete a strong musky odor. Herd members stand head to tail, vigorously rubbing scent on each other from this gland until all members share the same odor. While moving or feeding, herd members can keep track of each other by the cloud of group scent that envelops them. This also helps a lost member find the rest of the herd. In addition, javelinas use this scent to mark territorial boundaries, rubbing their backs on rocks, trees, or bushes. During summer months the animals are primarily nocturnal, bedding down under large mesquite trees or other shaded areas during the day; in winter they may be more active during the day. Javelinas have a poorly insulated, coarse, bristly fur, and they often huddle together in bed grounds to keep warm on particularly cold winter nights. Javelinas may also use small caves, mineshafts, or road culverts for shelter if they are available.

TRACK

← 1½" →

Javelina

COMMENTS
Mule deer prefer to make their own beds rather than borrow, but their beds could be mistaken for javelina beds. With deer there are usually only one or two beds together (about 18 by 30 inches each), not large group beds. Although the soil is loose, it is usually less disturbed than in a javelina bed. (See next page for more information on mule deer beds.)

BORROWERS
none known

KEY FEATURES
- ► large, shallow depressions
- ► oval shape
- ► about 18 by 30 inches or larger
- ► often under a bush or tree

POSSIBLE BUILDER
mule deer (*Odocoileus hemionus*)

DESCRIPTION OF DEPRESSION
Mule deer beds are typically much less disturbed looking than javelina beds. There are usually only a few shallow oval beds around the base of a bush or tree, rather than the many found with javelinas. Each bed is around 18 inches wide by about 30 inches or more long.

Mule deer

NATURAL HISTORY

Mule deer are the commonly seen deer in southern desert regions, while white tail deer live higher up on the mountains. Mule deer are ungulates, walking on their hooved toes. This extends the length of the leg, giving them a longer stride and an improved ability to run fast and escape predators. Mule deer tend to bound away with a stiff-legged bounce when disturbed, leaving deep tracks about 8 feet apart. Their tracks may be confused with those of javelinas, but the mule deer's track is longer, with pointed tips and a longer stride.

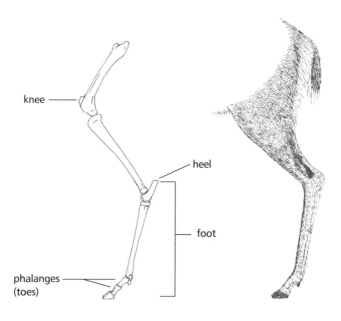

Deer walk on their toes, as shown above.

85

Mule deer are browsers, feeding on mesquite leaves and beans, catclaw, jojoba, buckbrush, fairy duster, and a variety of forbs and grasses. Their home range varies but is probably around 2 square miles, usually with water available within a mile or so. Within that area the deer have a number of different bedding spots, depending on weather, wind, and other factors. In the summer heat deer prefer a thickly vegetated and shaded area. On a cold winter day they may choose a sunny place just below a hill or ridge top out of the wind, but with a view of the area so they can watch for predators. They also pick high spots where the scents will drift upward to them on the air currents—an early warning system that enables them to smell approaching predators. Mule deer also move seasonally in short vertical migrations up and down the mountains.

The mule deer rut, or breeding season, is from December through January. Bachelor groups remain together until the rut, then the bucks become solitary and begin to fight. The rutting season is a great time to see sign, like bushes that bucks have attacked or used to rub off their velvet, or disturbed soil where they have been pushing, shoving, and fighting with each other. After breeding, a doe usually has one or two spotted fawns during the summer rainy season, July to September.

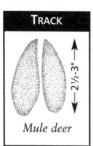

TRACK

2½–3"

Mule deer

BORROWERS
none known

KEY FEATURES
- ➤ disturbed soil from under 2 inches to 6 inches or more in diameter
- ➤ inverted cone shapes
- ➤ shallow to 3 inches or so deep

POSSIBLE BUILDER

curve-billed thrasher (*Toxostoma curvirostre*)
ground squirrels (*Spermophilus tereticaudus, Ammospermophilus harrisii*)
skunks (*Spilogale gracilis, Mephitis* spp., *Conepatus mesoleucus*)
coyote (*Canis latrans*), fox (*Vulpes* spp.), badger (*Taxidea taxus*)

DESCRIPTION OF DEPRESSION

Divots are usually sign of an animal digging for insects or seeds. They are not very deep, up to about 3 to 6 inches. The soil is loose and disturbed, and there are usually several divots in an area.

NATURAL HISTORY

Curve-billed thrashers are omnivorous and always investigating everything in their search for food. When you see the dirt thrown out of sidewalk cracks, or your potted plants pulled out of their pots and discarded, it's often the work of thrashers. They make divots of up to 2 inches in the desert soil as they dig up insects or grubs. They also use their bills like sickles, slashing about in leaf litter and debris after insects.

Ground squirrels often dig small, shallow divots about 1½ to 2 inches in diameter as they search for seeds. The dirt is usually thrown backwards out of the hole as they dig, so the hole is not round as much as slanting.

Skunks are great diggers, searching for insects and grubs. As a skunk digs, it turns in a circle so dirt is thrown out all around the hole, making an inverted cone shape about 2 to 4 inches in diameter.

Badgers, coyotes, and foxes all dig after rodents, leaving holes about 6 inches or larger. Usually these divots are at or near a packrat

Coyote

house, squirrel burrow, or mouse hole, and a considerable amount of dirt is moved. Sometimes claw marks or tracks in the loose soil can indicate who the digger was.

BORROWERS
If the divot is large enough and in fine soil, birds may use it for a dust bath.

KEY FEATURES
- ▶ about 7 to 9 inches long, less than 1 inch to 5 inches deep
- ▶ in fine, dusty soil
- ▶ no pebbles or rocks in depression

POSSIBLE BUILDER
almost all desert birds
kangaroo rats and other rodents
rabbits

DESCRIPTION OF DEPRESSION
Dust baths are found in fine, dry soil along trails or open spots where birds, rodents, and rabbits use the dirt to clean their feathers or fur. They vary in size from shallow scrapes to 6 to 9 inches deep. Evidence of bird tracks or rodent footprints are frequently seen around the baths.

Gambel's quail having a dust bath

Natural History

Birds spend a great deal of time maintaining their feathers, keeping them clean and free of parasites. Even if birds

Track

2"

Quail

bathe in water, they will still enjoy a good dust bath periodically. The dirt works well in absorbing excess oils and may help in removing parasites. Quail, cactus wrens, thrashers, doves, and other desert birds use dust baths several times a week, depending on soil temperature and moisture content. They prefer a warm, dry, fine dirt. All the birds will use the same bath, one after the other, although several baths might be found near each other if the soil is suitable.

Kangaroo rats have an aversion to wet fur, using dust baths instead to keep their oily coats clean and shiny. Other rodents and rabbits also use dust baths.

Borrowers
none known

MOUNDS

KEY FEATURES
- ▶ mounds of dirt with no entrance hole
- ▶ several mounds in an area
- ▶ in alluvial soils
- ▶ varying shapes to the mounds

POSSIBLE BUILDER
Botta's pocket gopher (*Thomomys bottae*)

DESCRIPTION OF HOLE
Pocket gophers dig extensive tunnel systems up to 90 to 200 feet long, pushing out piles of dirt periodically. These mounds can be oblong shapes or rounded mounds about 6 inches high and 8 to 16 inches in diameter. The exit hole is covered over with a cap of dirt.

NATURAL HISTORY
Pocket gophers spend most of their lives underground in their tunnels. There, safe from predators, they can access food in the form of roots and tubers, grasses, and other plants, which they pull down into the tunnel. They also eat roots and pads of prickly pear cactus. They live in easily diggable soil like riparian areas, golf courses, farms, or washes and are found at all elevations, but not usually in the caliche soils of the desert. Pocket gophers rarely visit the surface, and then don't stray far from their burrows. Usually they only emerge a few feet and quickly retreat backwards into the hole if danger threatens. Their naked tails are very sensitive and help the gophers feel their way as they travel backwards in tunnels that are too narrow to turn around in.

There isn't normally a lot of activity obvious at gopher

mounds, but sometimes you can see one pop its head out of the hole to dump a load of dirt from the tunnel. On other occasions plants can be seen disappearing into the ground as the gopher pulls them under.

Since pocket gophers are active year round, they often store bulbs and plant material in different chambers off the tunnel for use during leaner times. Different chambers are used for bathrooms and nest areas. When the bathrooms are full they are sealed off and another started elsewhere.

Gopher mounds

Pocket gophers dig their 90 to 200 foot long tunnels with the long claws on their front feet; they can also use their front teeth, which grow continuously and must be kept trimmed by regular gnawing. Their lips close behind the teeth so they don't get dirt in their mouths. Pocket gophers are solitary, only visiting each other during the breeding season when males and females might be found in the same burrow. Gophers and other burrowing creatures provide a very useful service by turning and aerating soil.

TRACKS

↕ 1¼"

Pocket gopher

BORROWERS

Gopher burrows are very popular places—rabbits, ground squirrels, mice, skunks, gopher snakes, rattlesnakes, lizards, and toads all make use of them. At higher elevations, even salamanders can be found in gopher burrows.

ELEVATED
HOLES

KEY FEATURES
- ► elliptical holes in dead or dying tree
- ► ⅛ to ¼ inch across
- ► plugged with leaves or resins and pebbles

POSSIBLE BUILDER
leafcutter bee (*Megachile sidalceae*)

DESCRIPTION OF HOLE
Although some leafcutter bee species dig
their own holes in the ground, most
don't, preferring to use abandoned holes
they find in trees. Wood boring beetles usually
leave a myriad of tiny exit holes in dead or decaying trees, especially palo verdes and mesquites.
These holes are just the right size (up to ¼ inch)
for leafcutter bee nests. If a hole is being used
by a leafcutter bee, either resin with pebbles
embedded in it or bits of leaves will be
evident sticking out of the hole.

*Leafcutter
bee and nest*

NATURAL HISTORY
There are many species of leafcutter bees in the Sonoran
Desert, some that emerge in the spring, others in the summer months. They mate after emerging,
and females immediately begin searching for a suitable hole to use as a nest
site. Then she flies around locating
broad-leafed plants like bougainvillea,
rosebushes, or other ornamentals, and
native plants like limberbush and various
legumes, and cuts elliptical or circular pieces

from the leaves to line her nest hole. She may use dozens of leaf pieces to stuff one hole. (Different species use plant resin with pebbles embedded in it instead of leaf pieces to line the hole; still others masticate the leaves into a dark green paste.) When the hole is prepared, she gathers nectar and pollen for bee bread, provisions the deep interior portion of the burrow, and lays an egg in the hole. She seals that cell with more leaves and begins on the next one until the beetle hole has 6 to 10 individual nest cells. The leafcutter bee then caps off the hole with a wad of 30 or more leaf pieces, some of which protrude out of the hole. The leafcutter bee may go on to provision another several beetle holes before she's done. She dies after laying the eggs. The larvae feed on the bee bread and grow, then spin cocoons and pupate inside the cell, overwintering and emerging the next spring.

Native leafcutter and mason bees can be encouraged to nest in a backyard by installing a bee house. These are simple blocks of wood with rows of holes ($^5/_{16}$ inch diameter) drilled into the block. Bee houses provide habitat to these gentle animals at a time when development and pesticide use are jeopardizing all of our native pollinators.

BORROWERS
none known

KEY FEATURES
- ► usually in a dead sotol, yucca, or agave stalk
- ► round to oval hole
- ► about ³⁄₈ to ½ inch

Possible Builder
carpenter bee (*Xylocopa* spp.)

Description of Hole
Carpenter bees like to excavate nest cavities in dead sotol, yucca, or agave stalks, but decaying logs, or any dry rotted wood will also do. The female chews a hole in the stalk to gain entrance, then excavates the pith, making a tunnel up to 10 or 12 inches long. Individual cells are then partitioned off for each egg she'll lay. During spring and summer, look for sawdust on the ground beneath the stalk where the carpenter bee is excavating.

Natural History
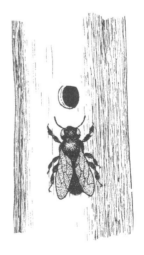

Carpenter bees are large black insects about the size of a bumblebee (about an inch in length), but the tops of carpenter bee abdomens do not have fuzzy hairs, giving the abdomens a shiny appearance. They are solitary bees, each female making and provisioning her own nest, although several carpenter bees may use the same area, or even the same stalk. After the female chooses a suitable dead stalk to use and excavates a tunnel inside it, she gathers pollen and nectar to make a paste of bee bread for the developing larva to eat. She places it in the bottom of the tunnel and lays an egg on it, then seals off that chamber with a mixture of sawdust and saliva and begins provisioning the next cell. The larvae feed on the ball of pollen and nectar, then pupate; the young bees finally emerging the following April or May. The last egg laid, a male (mother bees and ants can control the sex of their offspring), hatches first, then flies off to search for other newly emerging females with which to breed. As each new bee emerges, the one in the cell beneath it chews through the cell wall barrier and emerges next.

Male carpenter bees may aggressively defend a territory around potential nest sites or foraging areas, but they can't sting since they lack a stinger, which is a modified ovipositor (egg-laying apparatus). The females, however, can sting repeatedly as their stinger is not barbed like a honey bee's, but they rarely sting without provocation. The adults feed on nectar and pollen and are attracted to a variety of flowers like yellow bells, desert willow, and ocotillo.

BORROWERS
none known

KEY FEATURES
- ► on plant stems or twigs
- ► 10 to 20 tiny jagged cuts in a line
- ► each cut about $1/8$ of an inch long

POSSIBLE BUILDER
cicada (*Diceroprocia apache*)

DESCRIPTION OF HOLE
During the summer months, female cicadas insert their eggs into plant stems or young, tender twigs and branches of trees, often mesquite, palo verde, or acacias. There will be a vertical line of small ragged cuts on the branch. Sometimes the cicadas' efforts cause the twig to die, pruning the tree slightly. Look for dying or dead branch tips during the summer and fall and examine the branch for signs of cicada cuts. Mesquite girdlers also cause branch tips to die back, but girdlers leave a circular cut around the circumference of the branch.

NATURAL HISTORY
Most everyone is familiar with cicadas from their loud, buzzing songs during the hot summer months. Male cicadas perch in a bush or tree, and vibrate membranes on their abdomens to make buzzing calls to attract females. They call during the heat of the day when predators, such as birds, are resting and less active. Cicadas can tolerate the heat because they are one of the very few insects known to sweat to cool themselves off! They feed on plant sap, sucking the juices from plant stems, which gives them a plentiful supply of valuable moisture to use for sweating.

The male cicada mates with as many females as possible in the few short weeks of his life. Female cicadas usually choose a branch of a tree or bush overhanging a prickly pear cactus or other plant in which to deposit their eggs. When the eggs hatch, the nymphs (immature forms) drop into the plant and dig their way into the ground underneath to feed on the roots. The nymphs spend three years growing underground, then emerge in May or June of the third year. They leave an emergence hole about ¾ inch in diameter. The nymphs climb a nearby bush or tree, shed their exoskeletons and become adults.

Cicadas stop singing when a potential predator, such as a person, approaches, making it more difficult to locate them. If a male cicada is found and attacked by a bird or grasshopper mouse, it "screams," vibrating its abdominal membranes to produce a noise loud enough to be painful to human ears. This may distract or disturb the predator enough to give the cicada a chance to escape. But this tactic doesn't seem to work well with cicada killer wasps—they paralyze the cicadas with their sting, abruptly ending the cicadas' call.

To find a cicada emergence hole, look for the shed brown exoskeleton of the cicada on a branch or shrub during May or June, then look on the ground nearby for the hole.

BORROWERS
none known

KEY FEATURES
- ► small oblong or square holes about ¼ to ¾ inch
- ► many horizontal and vertical rows of holes around the trunk of a tree

POSSIBLE BUILDER
sapsucker (*Sphyrapicus* spp.)

DESCRIPTION OF HOLE
Sapsuckers drill exploration holes in a tree to see if they hit sap. When they do they drill below the hole in vertical rows. The holes vary slightly in shape and size, and usually encircle the tree.

NATURAL HISTORY
Sapsuckers are woodpeckers that drill rows of holes in a variety of trees like cottonwood, willow, aspen, and sycamore causing sap to well up in the holes. They feast on the nutritious and sweet sap, using the brushy tips of their tongues to slurp up the liquid. The sap also attracts insects like fruit flies, ants, butterflies, moths, and bees, which the sapsucker then eats. These birds also supplement their diet with fruits and berries.

Hummingbirds, warblers, verdins, and other birds are also attracted to the sap, but the sapsucker defends his sap wells against them. The other birds sneak in when the sapsucker is busy elsewhere. The sapsucker has to tend the wells, since they begin to heal over on the tree. It either reopens them or drills new wells. Sometimes the flow of sap to a limb is compromised and may cause that branch to die.

Sapsucker and rows of holes

Sapsuckers usually live at higher elevations in pine forests, but they do visit lower deciduous riparian habitats in the desert Southwest. Red-naped sapsuckers are the most commonly seen sapsucker in these areas, where their favorite trees are cottonwood, netleaf hackberry, walnut, ironwood, and mesquite. Apple and other fruit trees are eagerly used if available.

These woodpeckers also dig 1¼ inch nest holes in trees that other cavity nesting birds depend on. They often choose a tree that has a fungal infection, making the wood softer to dig out. Both the male and female help in excavating the nest hole, and both parents feed and care for the young, with the male incubating at night, the female during the day.

Borrowers

Many other birds and insects enjoy the sap, especially warblers, nuthatches, hummingbirds, and insects. Other cavity nesting birds use the abandoned nest holes.

KEY FEATURES
- ► circular or elliptical holes in dead or dying trees
- ► varying hole sizes from ⅛ to ¼ or ⁵⁄₁₆ inch
- ► usually many holes in the tree

Possible Builders
longhorn beetles (Cerambicidae family)
mesquite girdler (*Oncideres rhodosticta*)

Description of Longhorn Beetle Holes
Longhorn beetles bore tiny circular holes, often called galleries, in dead or dying trees. Dead palo verdes for example, will be riddled with dozens of beetle holes of varying sizes around the tree. The holes extend back into the center of the tree several inches.

Natural History of Wood Boring Beetles
There are many species of wood boring beetles in the desert Southwest, among them the palo verde root borer, the mesquite borer, and the mesquite girdler. Most have similar habits and lifestyles. The female beetle lays her eggs just under the bark of the tree, usually a dead or dying tree because live trees usually have chemical defenses against wood boring insects, and because dead wood is softer to chew. The eggs hatch and the larvae begin burrowing their way into the wood, eating as they go. Wood is not a very nutritious substance; insects that eat it generally spend a long time in the larval state, trying to grow large enough to pupate into adults. The wood boring beetles are unusual in that they can actually digest cellulose due to microorganisms in their gut, a feat few other animals can accomplish. Some of the wood boring beetles are preyed

upon by woodpeckers who can hear the larva inside the wood as they chew, and use their strong beaks to chisel in after them.

DESCRIPTION OF MESQUITE GIRDLER HOLES
The mesquite girdler leaves a deep groove of about $1/16$ to $1/8$ inch wide around a branch tip. Many tiny elongated exit holes, about $1/4$ inch in size, are scattered along the branch.

NATURAL HISTORY OF MESQUITE GIRDLERS
Many dead mesquite branch tips in an area indicates the presence of mesquite girdlers. Female girdlers emerge toward the end of the summer rainy season, mate, and begin girdling the smaller branch tips of mesquite trees (up to 2 inches or so). The girdler chews a groove around the branch to kill it, then lays her eggs in the dying branch tip. She kills the branch to stem the flow of sap so the larvae don't drown in it. The eggs hatch and the new larvae burrow into and feed on the cambium layer of the branch, progressing into the deeper wood as they grow. They pupate inside the branch, overwintering and emerging as adults the next year, leaving $1/8$ to $1/4$ inch exit holes in the dead mesquite branch.

Other wood boring beetles often usurp the dead mesquite branch the girdler so carefully prepared, laying their own eggs there. The eggs of the interloper hatch more quickly than the girdler's eggs, and they outcompete the girdler's progeny, taking over the branch.

BORROWERS
Leafcutter bees use the holes left in tree trunks by the beetles as they exit.

KEY FEATURES
- ▶ most commonly located in a saguaro cactus, less often in cottonwood or mesquite
- ▶ about 2 to 2½ inches or more in diameter

POSSIBLE BUILDERS

Gila woodpecker (*Melanerpes uropygialis*)
gilded flicker (*Colaptes chrysoides*)

DESCRIPTION OF HOLE

Most saguaros might have one or two woodpecker holes in them but some big, old saguaros may look like woodpecker condos with 30 or more nest holes. The entrance hole is around 2½ inches wide by 2 or 3 inches tall, although some may be larger, up to 4 inches. The hole is considerably larger inside the cactus, anywhere from 8 to 15 inches deep by 6 to 8 inches wide. When the saguaro dies and its soft tissue has decayed away, the hardened shell or "boot" that formed around the nest cavity can be seen lying on the ground or still attached to the saguaro skeleton.

NATURAL HISTORY

Both Gila woodpeckers and gilded flickers are year-round desert residents in wooded riparian areas, desert habitats, and suburbs. They establish a home territory, preferably with several saguaros in it, which they defend from other woodpeckers. Males like to drum loudly in spring to advertise their territorial boundaries.

Woodpeckers are fruit and insect eaters. They have a good sense of hearing and listen for insects chewing inside the wood, then use their strong sharp bills to chisel them out of tree trunks.

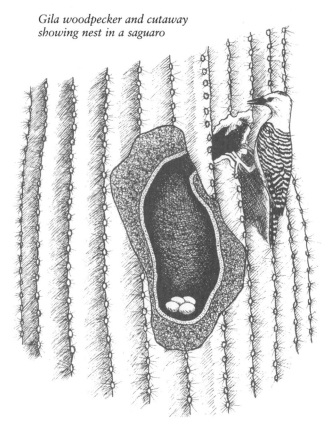

Gila woodpecker and cutaway showing nest in a saguaro

The male woodpecker excavates a nest hole in a saguaro. The saguaro secretes a sap that hardens or scabs over into a shell or "boot," sealing itself off from the hole. Once the cavity is dry it is ready for use. Gila woodpeckers typically use the middle portions of the saguaro. They dig into the soft tissue between the saguaro's outer skin and the woody ribs inside. The larger gilded flicker, with a heavier bill, digs into the top of the saguaro, right through the woody ribs into the center of the cactus. Sometimes this damages or kills the saguaro tip, but the cactus is usually able to live; growth continues from the arms.

After mating, the female woodpecker lays eggs in the boot without adding any nesting material. Both parents feed and care for the nestlings. Active woodpecker nests are not hard to find, as the nestlings are particularly loud and insistent; you can usually hear them calling for food from inside the nest hole from quite a distance away.

BORROWERS

Woodpecker holes are a center of life and activity. Well insulated, basically impervious to predators, and with a great view, they are valuable real estate and in great demand in palo verde-saguaro forests. Any cavity nesting bird of appropriate size—elf owls, screech owls, purple martins, sparrows, starlings, or kestrels—will use the holes. Even bats have been seen using saguaro holes.

BORROWED/
MODIFIED
SHELTERS

KEY FEATURES
- ➤ natural crevice under a boulder or in rock niche
- ➤ may be modified
- ➤ tortoise den or mammal burrow may be used

POSSIBLE OCCUPANT
Gila monster (*Heloderma suspectum*)

DESCRIPTION OF SHELTER
Gila monsters may dig their own burrows but more often borrow the dens of others, like a packrat house or ground squirrel burrow. In winter Gila monsters seek out different shelters for hibernation. These are most often south facing holes near or under boulders. Winter dens may be quite extensive. They may share particularly good den sites with other Gila monsters, or move in with a tortoise or snake.

NATURAL HISTORY
The Gila monster is one of the most unusual reptiles in the world, being one of only two venomous lizards known (the other is its cousin the Mexican beaded lizard). Gila monsters inhabit the mountain foothills and bajadas of the palo verde-saguaro forest, and its canyons, washes, and arroyos. They prefer rocky areas with boulders and plenty of places to hide. Although they are not uncommon in their range, Gila monsters are not often seen by people, because they spend more than 90% of their lives resting in underground burrows. They become active and may be seen during the day in the milder temperatures of March, April, and May, but become more crepuscular (active in the evening and early morning) and occasionally are

113

nocturnal during the summer rainy season.

The large (up to 1½ feet), heavy-bodied lizards are predators, but because they move fairly slowly, they eat newborn mice, round-tailed ground squirrels, Harris' antelope squirrels, and other rodents, as well as baby rabbits, bird and reptile eggs, and other food items that are easy to procure. Gila monsters can eat 35% of their body weight in one meal, storing the excess as fat in the tail. This fat sustains Gila monsters through inactive times and during winter hibernation. Because of their quiet lifestyles, Gila monsters can probably survive a year on just a few meals. Gila monsters differ from most lizards in that their tails do not detach or grow back, and they do not tolerate heat well. Most lizards have a skin that is basically impervious to water loss, and they can be active at quite warm temperatures, but Gila monsters do lose water through their skin, making them susceptible to dehydration.

Gila monsters are easily recognized by their bright black and pink coloring and beaded skin. In the sunlight this striking coloration works well as a warning, advertising that these lizards are venomous, while in the mottled shade the broken pattern effectively disguises the animals.

Although Gila monsters are venomous, they primarily bite in self-defense. The only way for a person to get bitten is to attempt to pick up or handle one of them. When provoked, the animal gapes its mouth and hisses, while backing up, trying to retreat to the safety of a patch of prickly pear or other cover. If molested further, the lizard can bite with impressive speed, hanging on with powerful jaws. Unlike the rattlesnake, which injects its venom and quickly retracts its fangs, a Gila monster envenomates by biting down on the victim with needle-sharp teeth that are covered by gums when not in use. On biting, glands in the

jaw release the venom to mix with saliva, which flow by
capillary action along grooves in the teeth into the wound.
As the Gila monster repeatedly bites down, more venom
flows into the wound, causing intense pain, swelling, and
hypotension. Gila monster venom affects blood pressure so
powerfully that it is now being studied for use as an anti-
hypertensive drug for people.

BORROWERS

Many creatures may share a Gila monster
den, including, tortoises,rattlesnakes,
other Gila monsters, or other lizards.

TRACK

↑
1¼"
↓

Gila monster

KEY FEATURES
> ► flat bottomed, half-moon shape hole
> ► up to 12 inches wide
> ► downward slope front to back

POSSIBLE OCCUPANT
desert tortoise (*Gopherus agassizii*)

DESCRIPTION OF SHELTER
Tortoise dens in the Sonoran Desert are most often found in sloping terrain such as hillsides and banks of washes, in rocky outcrops, or under bushes. The half-moon shape is usually distinctive. In southern Arizona tortoise dens may not be very deep (the tortoise may even be visible inside), as the winters are fairly mild, but some dens will extend to 6 feet or more. Tortoises are well equipped with claws on the front feet to dig their own burrows, but they often modify an existing rock crevice or animal burrow.

Desert tortoise and den

Natural History

Desert tortoises use dens in winter for hibernation. The den may be occupied by one tortoise or shared by two. They are most active during the spring, grazing on the succulent new green vegetation and wildflowers. During the summer drought and heat of June, they usually retire underground to estivate until the rains bring cooler temperatures and fresh vegetation to eat. The females remain more active during the summer than do male tortoises, perhaps needing to forage for additional nutrition for developing eggs. (Female tortoises dig a nest for egg laying in July but these holes are then covered over and are not obvious.) Tortoise dens are reused for many years and may be shared with other tortoises.

Comments

See the Depressions section for the life history of the desert tortoise.

Borrowers, Commensal Users

Many other animals, for example snakes, Gila monsters, other lizards, spiders, and other invertebrates, take advantage of a tortoise burrow, sharing it even while the tortoise is in residence.

Track

Desert tortoise

KEY FEATURES
- ▶ burrow in flat, open areas
- ▶ burrows lined with cow or horse dung or other debris
- ▶ small mound of dirt around hole entrance

POSSIBLE OCCUPANT
burrowing owl (*Athene cunicularia*)

DESCRIPTION OF SHELTER
Burrowing owls appropriate the burrows and dens of prairie dogs, ground squirrels, kit foxes, kangaroo rats, coyotes, and tortoises, modifying the shelters to suit their needs and preferences (see book cover). The entrance hole can be anywhere from 4 inches on up. The burrows always turn a corner into the nest chamber, perhaps to diminish light and heat radiating into the nest. The owls line the burrow with bits of horse or cow dung, food remains, feathers, and debris. This may be to disguise their scent to predators or as decoration. There is often a mound of dirt or a dead branch outside the hole where the owls like to perch.

NATURAL HISTORY
Burrowing owls are unusual in being the only owl or raptor to den and nest in underground burrows. They reside in open habitat such as desertscrub, grassland, prairie dog towns, airports, open fields, golf courses, and disturbed areas. They have very good eyesight and like to be where they have a clear view to watch for predators. In our warm climate the owls are permanent residents, though they migrate in cooler areas. They prey on rodents

(such as kangaroo rats), arthropods (beetles, moths, scorpions, grasshoppers), baby ground squirrels, prairie dog pups, toads, and young snakes and other small reptiles.

They hunt and call mostly at dusk, but they are different from other owls in being active during the daytime. Often a whole family stands around outside the den until the midday heat forces them to retire underground. The family may include up to seven owlets in good years, though most usually fall prey to predators. Because they are ground nesters, the burrowing owl chicks are susceptible to snakes, badgers, and coyotes. But the owls have a clever defense: When frightened or disturbed in their den, they imitate the sound of a rattlesnake's rattle, causing most predators to reconsider their plans. Parent owls also hover over predators, hissing, and diving on them to protect the nest, or they may bob up and down to draw attention to themselves, then fly off, distracting the predator from the nest.

Unfortunately burrowing owl populations are rapidly declining due to habitat loss from development, but they still use disturbed areas that are kept free of thick vegetation, like the berms along irrigation ditches or old cattle tanks. Experiments with providing artificial burrows of PVC or cement pipe leading to a buried nest box have been successful, with owls moving in almost immediately, so there is hope that we can maintain or increase burrowing owl populations in the desert Southwest.

BORROWERS
Many of the holes burrowing owls use collapse over time, but while they are open, snakes, wood rats and other rodents, and many insects will use a burrowing owl burrow.

KEY FEATURES
► in rock piles, under tree roots and buildings
► about 6 inches in diameter
► musky odor

POSSIBLE OCCUPANTS
spotted skunk (*Spilogale gracilis*)
striped skunk (*Mephitis mephitis*)
hooded skunk (*Mephitis macroura*)
hognose skunk (*Conepatus mesoleucus*)

DESCRIPTION OF SHELTER
Skunks den up in rock piles, crevices, caves, mine shafts, under tree roots, in brush piles, in streamside banks, in hollow logs, and under buildings, so there is no set description of skunk shelters, except that the holes they dig are about 6 inches in diameter. They may dig their own den or borrow the burrow of a fox, badger, ground squirrel, or packrat. Skunks also leave evidence of their activity in an area by their many divots and rootings.

NATURAL HISTORY
Arizona is blessed with all four species of skunks, owing to the great diversity of habitats in our state. All are omnivores and opportunistic feeders, eating insects (especially beetles, grubs, and grasshoppers), lizards, snakes, rodents, birds and bird eggs, carrion, seeds, and fruit, including prickly pear fruit. Parts of wing covers and beetle exoskeletons are often found in skunk scats.

They are nocturnal predators whose bold black and white patterns advertise their malodorous capabilities.

(Bright or dramatic coloring, called aposematic coloring, is often used to warn other creatures that an animal is venomous or dangerous in some way.) Because they are nocturnal the black and white coloring shows up better than bright colors would. Aside from automobiles—skunks reflect red eyeshine in car headlight— skunks do have one major predator: the great horned owl. Owls don't mind being sprayed with skunk scent at all, since they have a very diminished (if any) sense of smell.

SPOTTED SKUNKS

The spotted is the smallest of our skunks, weighing in at only 1 to 2 pounds. They are easy to distinguish from the other skunks by the several broken white stripes that give the animal its spotted appearance. The tail is black at the base and white at the tip. They occur most frequently in rocky canyons and riparian habitats. This is the only skunk that can climb trees.

Spotted skunks are placid, easy going animals, and are reluctant to spray unless strongly provoked. They stamp their feet as a warning when annoyed. If this is not heeded they proceed to do a handstand arching the back to aim at the predator's face. Skunks don't like the odor of their spray any more than other animals do, and if they cannot get their tail out of the way, they are hesitant to spray and chance getting the odor on themselves.

Spotted skunks breed in the fall but delayed implantation results in the four or five kits being born in the spring. The kits stay with the mother for several months, following her on hunting expeditions at night, before dispersing in the fall.

STRIPED SKUNKS

The striped is our most common skunk, a large-sized skunk weighing about 4 to 10 pounds. They inhabit a wide variety of habitats and elevations, including wooded areas and thickets, riparian areas, and farmland, even ranging up to the oaks and pines. They're also often found in cities at parks and garbage dumps. They are usually absent from the driest areas. Skunks don't hibernate, though they may retire for a few days during winter storms.

Spotted skunk and hole

HOODED SKUNKS

Of all the skunks, the hooded has the longest, most beautiful tail, which looks like a large white plume. They are less common than the striped skunk, though the two are often confused. The hooded can be told apart by its long tail and the ruff of fur about the neck. In addition, hooded skunks are found primarily in rocky canyons and washes but not in the low deserts.

HOGNOSE SKUNKS

The least common of our skunks, the hognose has a bare patch on his nose, and roots around in the leaf litter and dirt for insects. It has longer claws on the front feet than the other skunks and is more specialized for digging in the soft ground for grubs and insects. The hognose is a creature of the mid to higher elevations.

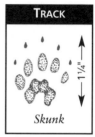

TRACK

1 1/4"

Skunk

BORROWERS
none known

FINE-TUNING YOUR SEARCH

Don't forget to observe your natural surroundings for additional clues. For instance, If you are in a lush canyon and find a fox den, you can be certain it belongs to a gray fox rather than a kit fox, who prefers the low, flat, open areas. Sometimes season will give a clue as to possible occupants. For example, in winter round-tailed ground squirrels, most reptiles, some insects and spiders, and certain mice are inactive and can therefore be eliminated as possibilities.

KEY FEATURES
> ► crevice or hole among rocks
> ► can be a mammal burrow
> ► sizes of holes vary considerably

POSSIBLE OCCUPANTS
rattlesnakes (*Crotalus* spp.)
other snakes

DESCRIPTION OF SHELTER
One of the most commonly asked questions about desert
holes is whether or not it's a snake hole. With the excep-
tion of snakes that burrow under loose soil or sand, snakes
don't build their own burrows. Instead, they borrow existing crevices in rocky outcrops, tortoise dens, or mammal
burrows, usually packrat dens, ground squirrel holes, or
mouse holes. While snakes are active (generally March
through October) they use any convenient retreat to escape
the day's heat or for safety, but with the onset of winter,
snakes seek out special places where they can hibernate.

NATURAL HISTORY
Because winters in the Sonoran Desert are not very severe
and there are plenty of rocky outcrops, mine shafts,
burrows, and other suitable shelters, snakes living here
tend to hibernate individually or in small groups (possibly
up to 30), unlike the huge aggregations of snakes that
occur in areas where den sites are few and all must share.
Good den sites are used year after year. Snake activity
picks up in October as many snakes gather before hibernation and begin moving slowly toward the dens, which are
not usually more than a mile away. The largest and oldest

snakes start back first, and they may leave scent trails that other snakes follow. Younger snakes may need to stay out as long as possible getting a few more meals and putting on more weight before retreating for the winter. Snakes tend to use the same established routes every year. Montezuma Castle National Monument's visitor center building was unknowingly constructed in the middle of a

Rattlesnake shelter

rattlesnake travel route to a hibernation den. Consequently every spring and fall large numbers of rattlers are encountered around the visitor center as the snakes travel to and from their hibernaculum. In the winter snakes may come out to the den entrance to sun and bask on warm days, but they are unable to hunt or eat during this time. With spring's warmer temperatures, the snakes begin moving and heading out to begin their season of activity.

BORROWERS, COMMENSAL USERS
Many other snakes share dens with rattlesnakes, including gopher snakes and racers. Tortoises and Gila monsters also don't mind sharing with snakes.

INDEX

FIELD NOTES

Field notes aid greatly in the gathering of data on animal movements and activity, as well as the scarcity or abundance of certain species in an area. Should you want to start your own field notebook, the following form should get you headed in the right direction.

FIELD OBSERVATION NOTES

DATE _____ TIME _____

OBSERVATION _____

_____

_____

_____

_____

_____

_____

WHERE SIGHTED _____

_____

WEATHER & TEMP _____

_____

OBSERVED BY _____

Field Notes

_____

_____

_____

_____

_____

_____

_____

_____

_____

_____

_____

_____

_____

_____

_____

_____

_____

_____

_____

_____

FIELD NOTES

INCHES CM